Radio Amateur
and
Listener's
Pocket Book

Newnes
Radio Amateur and Listener's Pocket Book

Steve Money G3FZX

Heinemann: London

Heinemann Professional Publishing Ltd
22 Bedford Square, London WC1B 3HH

LONDON   MELBOURNE   JOHANNESBURG   AUCKLAND

First published 1987

Bristish Library Cataloguing in Publication Data
Money, Steve A.
   Radio amateur and listener's pocket book.
   1. Amateur radio stations   2. Radio –
   Apparatus and supplies
   I. Title
   621.3841'51   TK9956

ISBN 0 434 91259 X

Typeset by Vision Typesetting, Manchester
Printed in Great Britain by
Butler & Tanner Ltd, Frome

Contents

Preface

Although conventional telephony and telegraphy are the most widely used communications techniques in amateur radio there has been, in recent years, an increase in interest in the more exotic forms of communication. Radioteletype (RTTY), amateur teletype over radio (AMTOR), slow scan television (SSTV) and more recently packet radio are communications techniques which have benefited from the widespread availability of home or personal computers which can be used to provide the decoding and display facilities for such transmissions. In this book a simple description is given of the principles involved in these modern communications techniques. Details are also given of the frequencies where such transmissions may be found.

With the coming of the space age radio amateurs were able to design and build their own space satellites which were launched into orbit as part of the payload when commercial satellites were launched. Early amateur satellites provided simple radio beacons but the current series are used to provide communications transponders which allow radio amateurs to achieve worldwide contacts via satellite using the VHF and UHF bands. Details of current satellites and the frequencies used are given in this book.

Radio enthusiasts may also be interested in receiving weather pictures from the numerous weather satellites now in orbit or receiving television transmissions from communications satellites and future direct broadcast TV satellites. This book gives details of these satellites and the frequencies they use.

The availability of scanner receivers and all band communications type receivers combined with the use of home computers has increased interest in listening to some of the wide variety of utility stations that operate on the HF, VHF and UHF bands. Among these are aircraft and maritime stations and also the various press agency stations which transmit news using radioteletype transmissions. Details of the bands where these stations are to be found and some sample frequencies are given in this book.

As an aid to operating I have also included much general information such as lists of call sign prefixes, both alphabetically and by country, useful abbreviations, such as Q codes, and general information on the principles of receivers, transmitters, antennas and propagation. The aim of this book has been to provide a useful quick reference for radio amateurs and listeners and a short bibliography has been included which will provide sources for more detailed information on some of the subjects covered in this book.

Steve Money
May 1987

1
Radio frequencies

Radio frequency band names

3–30 kHz	Very low frequency (VLF)
30–300 kHz	Low frequency (LF)
300–3000 kHz	Medium frequency (MF)
3–30 MHz	High frequency (HF)
30–300 MHz	Very high frequency (VHF)
300–3000 MHz	Ultra high frequency (UHF)
3–30 GHz	Super high frequency (SHF)
Above 30 GHz	Extra high frequency (EHF)

Radio wavelength band names

10 000–100 000 m	Myriametric (VLF)
1000–10 000 m	Kilometric (LF)
100–1000 m	Hectometric (MF)
10–100 m	Decametric (HF)
1–10 m	Metric (VHF)
10 cm–1 m	Decimetric (UHF)
1–10 cm	Centimetric (SHF)
0·1–1 cm	Millimetric (EHF)
0·01–0·1 cm	Decimillimetric (EHF)

Microwave band designations

European (NATO) microwave bands

1·0–2·0 GHz	L band
2·0–4·0 GHz	S band
4·0–8·0 GHz	C band
7·0–12 GHz	X band
12–18 GHz	J band
18–26 GHz	K band
26–40 GHz	Q band
40–60 GHz	V band
60–90 GHz	O band

USA microwave bands

0·4–1·5 GHz	L band
1·5–5·2 GHz	S band
3·7–6·2 GHz	C band
5·2–10·9 GHz	X band
10·9–36 GHz	K band
11·7–12·7 GHz	Ku band
36–46 GHz	Q band
46–56 GHz	V band
56–100 GHz	W band

Frequency-wavelength conversion

Frequency, $f \quad = \dfrac{300}{\lambda}$ MHz

Wavelength, $\lambda \quad = \dfrac{300}{f}$ m

Comité Consultatif International de Télèphonie et de Télègraphie (CCITT) regions

Worldwide administration of radio is divided up into three major regions as follows:

Region 1   Europe, Africa and Russia
Region 2   Asia and Oceania
Region 3   North and South America

Frequency allocations and band usage vary slightly between the three regions.

General frequency allocations

VLF, LF, MF (frequency in kHz)

10·0–140·5	Fixed; maritime; navigation
140·5–283·5	Broadcast
255·0–526·5	Radio navigation; fixed
526·0–1606·5	Broadcast
1606·5–1800·0	Maritime and land mobile; fixed
1810·0–1850·0	Amateur (shared in UK)
1850–2000	Amateur
1850–2045	Fixed; mobile
2045–2173·5	Maritime mobile; fixed
2160–2170	Radiolocation
2173·5–2190·5	Mobile
2190·5–2194	Maritime
2194–2625	Fixed; mobile
2300–2498	Broadcast
2625–2650	Maritime mobile
2650–2850	Fixed; mobile
2850–3155	Aero mobile

HF (frequency in kHz)

3155–3400	Fixed; mobile
3200–3400	Broadcast
3400–3500	Aero mobile
3500–3800	Amateur, fixed; mobile
3800–4000	Amateur (region 2 only)
3800–3900	Fixed; mobile
3800–3950	Aero mobile
3950–4000	Fixed; broadcast
4000–4063	Fixed; maritime mobile

4063–4438	Maritime mobile
4438–4650	Fixed; mobile
4650–4750	Aero mobile
4750–5060	Fixed; mobile; broadcast
5060–5480	Fixed; mobile
5450–5730	Aero mobile
5730–5950	Fixed; mobile
5950–6200	Broadcast
6200–6525	Maritime mobile
6525–6765	Aero mobile
6765–7000	Fixed; mobile
7000–7100	Amateur
7100–7300	Amateur (region 2 only)
7100–7300	Broadcast (regions 1 and 3)
7300–8195	Fixed
8100–8815	Maritime mobile
8815–9040	Aero mobile
9040–9500	Fixed
9500–10 000	Broadcast
10 000–10 100	Aero mobile
10 100–11 175	Fixed
10 100–10 150	Amateur
11 175–11 400	Aero mobile
11 400–11 650	Fixed
11 650–12 050	Broadcast
12 050–12 230	Fixed
12 230–13 200	Maritime mobile
13 200–13 360	Aero mobile
13 360–13 600	Fixed
13 600–13 800	Broadcast
13 800–14 000	Fixed
14 000–14 350	Amateur
14 350–15 000	Fixed
15 000–15 100	Aero mobile
15 100–15 600	Broadcast
15 600–16 360	Fixed
16 360–17 410	Maritime mobile
17 410–17 550	Fixed
17 550–17 900	Broadcast
17 900–18 030	Aero mobile
18 030–18 068	Fixed
18 068–18 168	Amateur
18 168–18 780	Fixed
18 780–18 900	Maritime mobile
18 900–19 680	Fixed
19 680–19 800	Maritime mobile
19 800–21 000	Fixed
21 000–21 450	Amateur
21 450–21 850	Broadcast
21 850–21 870	Fixed
21 870–22 000	Aero mobile
22 000–22 855	Maritime mobile
22 855–23 200	Fixed; mobile
23 200–23 350	Aero mobile
23 350–24 890	Fixed; mobile
24 890–24 990	Amateur
25 010–25 070	Fixed; mobile
25 070–25 210	Maritime mobile

21 210–25 550	Fixed; mobile
25 550–25 670	Radio astronomy
25 670–26 100	Broadcast
26 100–26 175	Maritime mobile
26 175–28 000	Fixed; mobile
28 000–29 700	Amateur
29 700–30 000	Fixed; mobile

VHF, UHF (frequencies in MHz)

30·0–50·0	Fixed; mobile
47·0–68·0	Broadcast (TV)
50·0–52·0	Amateur (UK)
50·0–54·0	Amateur (regions 2 and 3)
68·0–74·8	Fixed; mobile
70·0–70·5	Amateur (UK)
74·8–75·2	Aero navigation
75·2–87·5	Fixed; mobile
87·5–108	Broadcast (FM)
108–118	Aero navigation
118–137	Aero mobile
137–138	Spacecraft; satellites
138–144	Aero mobile; space research
144–146	Amateur
146–148	Amateur (regions 2 and 3 only)
146–174	Fixed; mobile
156–174	Maritime mobile
174–230	Broadcast (TV)
220–225	Amateur (USA)
230–328·6	Fixed; mobile
328·6–335·4	Aero navigation
335·4–400	Fixed; mobile
400–410	Space research; meteorology
410–430	Fixed; mobile
430–440	Amateur; radiolocation
440–470	Fixed; mobile
470–855	Broadcast (TV)
855–1300	Fixed; mobile
902–928	Amateur (USA)
934–935	Citizens band (UK)
1240–1325	Amateur
1300–1350	Aero navigation
1350–1400	Fixed; mobile
1400–1429	Space (uplink); fixed
1429–1525	Fixed; mobile
1525–1600	Space (downlink)
1600–1670	Space (uplink)
1670–1710	Space (downlink)
1710–2290	Fixed; mobile
2290–2300	Space (downlink); fixed
2300–2450	Amateur; fixed
2310–2450	Amateur (UK)
2300–2500	Fixed; mobile
2500–2700	Fixed; space (downlink)
2700–3300	Radar
3300–3400	Radiolocation; amateur
3400–3600	Fixed; space (uplink)
3600–4200	Fixed; space (downlink)
4200–4400	Aero navigation

4400–4500	Fixed; mobile
4500–4800	Fixed; space (downlink)
4800–5000	Fixed; mobile
5000–5850	Radio navigation; radar
5650–5850	Amateur
5850–7250	Fixed; space (uplink)
7250–7900	Fixed; space (downlink)
7900–8500	Fixed; mobile; space
8500–10 500	Radar; navigation
10 000–10 500	Amateur
10 700–12 700	Space (downlink); fixed
12 700–15 400	Space (uplink); fixed
17 700–20 000	Space (up/down); fixed
24 000–24 250	Amateur

Emission designations

The standard emission definitions adopted by the CCIR (Comité Consultatif International de Radiocommunication) consists of up to five symbols although for most applications only the first three are normally used. The first symbol indicates the type of modulation being used. The second symbol is a number which indicates the type of modulating signal being used and the third symbol is a letter which indicates the type of information being conveyed by the modulating signal. These are specified as follows:

First symbol: type of modulation of carrier

N   Unmodulated carrier
A   Double sideband amplitude modulated
H   Single sideband full carrier
J   Single sideband suppressed carrier
R   Single sideband reduced carrier
B   Independent sideband modulation
C   Vestigial sideband AM
F   Frequency modulation
G   Phase modulation
P   Unmodulated pulses
K   Amplitude modulated pulses
L   Width or duration modulated pulses
M   Position or phase modulated pulses
X   Cases not otherwise covered

Second symbol: type of modulating signal

0   No modulating signal
1   Single digital channel
2   Single digital channel using subcarrier
3   Single analogue channel
7   Multichannel digital signal
8   Multichannel analogue signal
9   Combination of 7 and 8

Third symbol: type of information

N   No information
A   Telegraphy (Morse)
B   Automatic telegraphy (radioteletype (RTTY) etc.)
C   Facsimile

D   Data transmission
E   Telephony
F   Television (includes slow scan television (SSTV))
W   Television with sound
X   Other signals

The fourth symbol is used to define the type of coding used for digital signals (letters A to F) or the type of sound or vision transmission (i.e. monophonic or stereophonic sound, monochrome or colour video) (letters G to X).

The fifth symbol is used to indicate if the channel is multiplexed and the type of multiplexing system used.

For most applications only the first three symbols of the emission designation are used. Commonly used modes are:

A1A   Morse using on-off keying (continuous wave (CW))
A2A   Morse using a keyed tone (modulated continuous wave (MCW))
A1B   RTTY using on-off keying
A2B   RTTY using on-off keyed tone
A3C   FAX using amplitude modulation (AM)
A3E   AM telephony (amplitude modulation)
A3F   Television or slow scan television using AM
C3F   Television AM vestigial sideband
J3E   Single sideband (SSB) suppressed carrier
F1A   Telegraphy by frequency shift keying (FSK)
F1B   FM radioteletype (FSK)
F2A   FM telegraphy by keyed audio tone
F2B   FM radioteletype with FSK audio frequency shift keying (AFSK) subcarrier
F3C   FAX using frequency modulation
F3E   FM telephony
F3F   Television or slow scan television using FM
G1B   Radioteletype using phase shift keying
G2B   Radioteletype with phase shift subcarrier
G3E   Phase modulated telephony
P0N   Unmodulated pulse transmission
R3E   Reduced carrier mode telephony

2
Amateur radio

Licensing in Great Britain

In Great Britain two classes of amateur radio licence are available.
The *class A* licence requires the operator to have passed the radio
amateur's examination and to have passed a Morse test
demonstrating the ability to send and receive Morse code at twelve
words per minute. This licence permits the user to operate on all
bands allocated for amateur radio use with all modes of transmission
including telegraphy, telephony, radioteletype, facsimile, television
and data transmissions.

The second type of licence is the *class B* licence for which the
applicant has to have passed the *radio amateur's examination*. This
licence permits operation of a transmitter on all amateur radio bands
above 30 MHz using all modes of transmission permitted by the class
A licence. If the holder of a class B licence goes on to take the Morse
test then a class A licence may be issued allowing the station to
operate on the HF amateur bands.

A class B licence holder is allowed to use the station of a class A
licence to operate on the HF bands provided this is done under the
supervision of the class A licensee and the call sign used is that of the
class A station. The class B licence holder must then sign the station
log to show that he or she was operating the station.

Licensing in the USA

In the USA there are four classes of amateur licence. The lowest grade
is the *novice level* which requires a technical examination and Morse
at five words per minute. Novices may use CW (continuous wave)
only operation on limited sections of the 3·5, 7, 21 and 28 MHz bands
with 200 watts input power. The *technician's licence* has a more
difficult technical exam with Morse at five words per minute and
allows use of all modes on the VHF and UHF bands as well as CW in
the novice sections of the HF bands. The standard level licence is the
general class which has the same technical examination as technician
class and a Morse test at thirteen words per minute. The general
licence permits phone and CW on all HF bands and all modes on
VHF/UHF with 1 kW input. By passing a further technical
examination the amateur can obtain an *advanced class licence* which
permits the use of higher power and more modes on the HF bands.
The highest licence level is the *extra class* giving all modes and bands.

Radio amateur's examination (RAE)

This is a technical examination organized by the City and Guilds of
London which examines the applicant for a basic knowledge of the
principles involved in radio transmission and reception and the rules
and conditions of the amateur radio licence. Particular emphasis is

placed on the knowledge of operation of equipment in a proper manner to avoid causing interference to other services.

The examination itself takes the form of a multiple choice questions paper in which three or four possible answers are given for each question. The student is then required to select the most appropriate answer for each question. This form of paper has the advantage that it can readily be marked by using computer techniques, thus reducing the time needed to evaluate the examination results. The examination takes place normally twice a year at a large number of centres throughout Great Britain.

Morse test

A class A licence applicant is required to pass a test demonstrating the ability to send and receive Morse at twelve words per minute. Tests are organized by the Radio Society of Great Britain (RSGB) on behalf of the Department of Trade and Industry. Tests are arranged at many locations in Britain throughout the year. Facilities for taking the Morse test are often provided at amateur radio rallies and conventions. Bookings for Morse tests are made in advance of the test date and applicants should contact the RSGB for a list of test venues and dates in order to book a Morse test.

For the test about thirty-six words of plain language text, often taken from a book or magazine, are sent using a standard Morse key connected to a buzzer or tone generator. Up to four corrections may be made while sending and all errors must be corrected. A similar plain language text must then be received and written on paper with less than four errors. The time allowed for each of these tests is three minutes. A further test involving sending and receiving ten groups of five figures is then made. Here the time for each test is one and a half minutes and only two errors or corrections are permitted. If the applicant satisfies the examiner that he or she is able to send and receive Morse correctly at the required speed a pass certificate is awarded.

Morse code

A	· —	N	— ·
B	— · · ·	O	— — —
C	— · — ·	P	· — — ·
D	— · ·	Q	— — · —
E	·	R	· — ·
F	· · — ·	S	· · ·
G	— — ·	T	—
H	· · · ·	U	· · —
I	· ·	V	· · · —
J	· — — —	W	· — —
K	— · —	X	— · · —
L	· — · ·	Y	— · — —
M	— —	Z	— — · ·

1	·————		6	—····
2	··———		7	——···
3	···——		8	———··
4	····—		9	————·
5	·····		0	—————

Query (?)	··——··
Stop (.)	·—·—·—
Hyphen (-)	—····—
Comma (,)	——··——
Slash (/)	—··—·
Error	········

Procedure codes (letter pairs sent as a single code)

Wait (AS)	·—···
End of contact (SK)	···—·—
Go ahead (K)	—·—
Over to specific station (KN)	—·——·
Over when calling station (AR)	·—·—·
Roger (all received ok) (R)	·—·
Closing down (CL)	—·—··—··

Morse code timing

Dot time is basic element	
Dash time	3 dots
Space between elements	1 dot
Space between characters	3 dots
Space between words	7 dots

Morse code transmission speed is normally measured in words per minute (w.p.m.). Speed calculations are based on an average word length of five characters and an average character length of 50 dot periods. Approximate dot times for typical Morse speeds are:

Words per minute	Dot time (ms)
6	200
12	100
18	67
24	50

Most amateur radio licence rules require a Morse speed of twelve words per minute for a HF band licence. Some countries have novice licences where a speed of perhaps six w.p.m. is required. Novice stations have restricted access to the HF bands and lower power limits.

Morse practice

Many amateur radio clubs run classes to teach newcomers how to send and receive Morse code in preparation for the Morse test. Class B stations are permitted to send and receive Morse signals on the

VHF bands as part of their training to upgrade to a full class A licence. Practice nets are often arranged by clubs to allow class B stations in the area to practise sending and receiving Morse code.

There are a number of regular broadcast transmissions of slow speed Morse for listeners and amateurs wishing to improve their ability to receive Morse code. These transmissions cover a range of speeds and normally include both plain language passages and mixed figure/letter groups.

Morse practice in Great Britain

Transmissions on HF and VHF are organized by local amateur radio clubs. Some regular HF band transmissions are:

G3GNS	RAF, Locking Avon	1910 kHz, 3550 kHz
		Mon., Wed., Thurs., Fri. 1830
		Tues., Sat., Sun. 1200
G4RS	Catterick, North Yorkshire	3565 kHz
		Tues., Thurs., 1900
G4PYR	Solihull, West Midlands	1888 kHz
		Sun., Mon. 1900
G40BK	Chorley, Lancashire	3565 kHz
		Fri. 1930
GM4HYF	Glasgow	28 350 kHz
		Wed. 2130, Thurs. 2200

Most VHF transmissions use 144·250 MHz (A1A) or 145250 (F2A) at various times between 1830 and 2200.

A full list of Morse practice transmissions for listeners in Britain is available from the Radio Society of Great Britain.

Morse practice from Veron (Holland)

Station PA0AA
3602 kHz, 14 103 kHz, 144·800 MHz, 433·45 MHz.
Fridays only:
1900–1930   for beginners
1930–2000   for advanced listeners

Morse practice from Amateur Radio Relay League (USA)

Station W1AW, Newington, Connecticut
1818 kHz, 3580 kHz, 7080 kHz, 14 070 kHz, 21 080 kHz, 28 080 kHz, 50 080 kHz.

5 to 15 words per minute:
Mon., Wed., Fri.	1400, 2400 GMT
Tues., Thurs., Sat., Sun.	2100 GMT
Wed., Fri., Sun., Mon.	0300 GMT

10 to 35 words per minute:
Tues., Thurs.	0300, 1400, 2400 GMT
Sat., Sun.	2400 GMT
Mon.	2100 GMT

Times are one hour earlier during summer months.

Amateur radio bands in Great Britain

HF bands class A stations only:

Frequency band	Carrier output (W)	Single sideband peak envelope power output (W)	Status
1810–2000 kHz	8	32	SEC
3500–3800 kHz	100	400	PRI
7000–7100 kHz	100	400	PRI
10 100–10 150 kHz	100	400	SEC
14 000–14 350 kHz	100	400	PRI
18 068–18 168 kHz	10	A1A (CW) only	SEC
21 000–21 450 kHz	100	400	PRI
24 890–24 990 kHz	10	A1A (CW) only	SEC
28 000–29 700 kHz	100	400	PRI

VHF, UHF and Microwave (class A and B stations)

Frequency band	Carrier output (W)	Single sideband peak envelope power output (W)	Status
50·0–51·0 MHz	25	100 e.r.p.*	PRI
51·0–52·0 MHz	25	100 e.r.p.*	SEC
70·0–70·5 MHz	40	160	SEC
144–146 MHz	100	400	PRI
430–432 MHz	10	e.r.p.* maximum	SEC
432–440 MHz	100	400	SEC

*Effective radiated power.

50 MHz band horizontally polarized antennas only.

Frequency band	DC input (W)	Single sideband peak envelope power input (W)	Status
1240–1325 MHz	150	400	SEC
2310–2450 MHz	150	400	SEC
3400–3475 MHz	150	400	SEC
5650–5680 MHz	150	400	SEC
5755–5765 MHz	150	400	SEC

Frequency band	DC input (W)	Single sideband peak envelope power input (W)	Status
5820–5850 MHz	150	400	SEC
10·00–10·50 GHz	150	400	SEC
24·00–24·05 GHz	150	400	PRI
24·05–24·25 GHz	150	400	SEC
47·00–47·20 GHz	150	400	PRI
75·50–76·00 GHz	150	400	PRI
142·0–144·0 GHz	150	400	PRI
248·0–250·0 GHz	150	400	PRI

PRI indicates a band allocated primarily for amateur use but the 3·5 MHz band is shared with other users on a non-interference basis.

SEC indicates a band allocated for amateur use on a secondary basis subject to non-interference with primary services operating in that band.

The emission modes permitted are:

CW (A1A, A2A, F1A, F2A, G1A, G2A) all bands.
RTTY (A1B, A2B, F1B, F2B, G1B, G2B) except 18 and 24 MHz.
Phone (A3E, J3E, F3E, G3E) except 18 and 24 MHz.
Fax (A3C, F3C, G3C) 3·5, 7, 14, 21, 28 and 50 MHz.
SSTV (A3F, C3F) 3·5, 7, 14, 21, 28 and 50 MHz only.
TV (A3F, C3F, F3F, G3F) above 432 MHz only.
Pulse modes on 2·4, 5·7, 5·8 and 10·0 GHz bands and on 47, 75, 142 and 250 GHz.

Third party traffic

Some countries, such as the USA, allow their amateur radio operators to handle messages for members of the public who are not licensed amateurs. In fact, many US amateurs handle radiogram messages on a non-commercial basis. Another regular activity is that of *phone patching* where a local member of the public can be linked to someone at a distance via amateur radio. Here the caller telephones the amateur at local call rates and the amateur tries to establish contact with another amateur in the town where the caller wishes to make a call. The second amateur then makes the local phone call and the phone conversation is then patched through the amateur radio link. This mode is often used by US servicemen in Europe making calls home to their families. This form of operation is known as handling third party traffic.

In Britain the licence does not permit the handling of messages for third parties by normal amateur stations. The exception is special event stations with GB call signs where it is permissible for non-licensed persons to send a simple greetings message to the station which is being contacted. This greetings message concession is used at events such as the Scouts' Jamboree on the air. In an emergency, amateur stations may handle messages for the emergency services.

Reciprocal licences

Reciprocal licensing agreements with many countries allow licensed amateurs from those countries to operate in Britain. These stations may be granted either class A or class B status depending upon the conditions associated with the licence held in their own country. The callsign used by such stations is normally a G prefix of the appropriate type followed by their own home callsign (e.g. G0/W2ABC).

Under these reciprocal arrangements British amateurs may obtain a licence to operate in foreign countries such as the USA and most European countries. The application for a reciprocal licence usually needs to be made well in advance of a visit and is normally made to the licensing authority of the country concerned. More details of reciprocal licensing arrangements may be obtained from the Radio Society of Great Britain.

Radio Amateur Emergency Network

The Radio Amateur Emergency Network (RAYNET) has been set up in Britain to provide assistance to the emergency services and the police when an emergency such as a flood occurs. The country is divided up into twelve regions each of which has a RAYNET regional organizer and a number of area organizers. In the event of an emergency occurring the members of the local network may be alerted and the amateurs then provide assistance with communications using amateur radio channels. Most of this communication is carried out on the VHF bands but for some international disasters such as earthquakes the HF bands may be used to provide contacts with the emergency area.

At regular intervals the RAYNET groups may take part in practice exercises in preparation for any real emergency that might occur. Apart from emergency use the RAYNET communications facilities may also be used at events such as marathon runs to provide communications for first aid requests or control of the event.

In the USA similar schemes have been set up by radio amateurs. These are the Amateur Radio Emergency Service (ARES) organized by Amateur Radio Relay League (ARRL) and the Radio Amateur Civil Emergency Service (RACES) which is part of the civil defence organization. Like RAYNET these amateur emergency services work in association with official services to provide communications assistance during emergencies or disasters.

Amateur radio rallies and conventions

In many countries radio amateurs get together during the year at
radio rallies and conventions. Rallies were initially developed as
meetings of amateur mobile operators and these rallies usually
feature trade and amateur radio stalls selling new or secondhand
equipment and components. Conventions feature a series of lectures
or demonstrations on a range of subjects of interest to radio
amateurs. Most conventions also have trade and club stalls. Some of
the larger rallies and conventions in Britain and America are as
follows:

March/April	RSGB National Convention, Birmingham
March/April	RSGB VHF Convention, Esher, Surrey
April	Dayton Hamvention, Dayton, Ohio, USA
July	Longleat Rally, near Warminster, Wiltshire
August	National Rally, Woburn Abbey, Bedfordshire

Jamboree on the air

The scouting movement worldwide has associated itself with amateur
radio and every year, for one weekend during October, radio
amateurs set up stations at scout camps and meeting halls to hold a
jamboree on the air. In many countries special permission is given to
allow the scouts themselves to pass messages and greetings to other
scout groups around the world. The radio jamboree also allows those
scouts taking tests in communications to work towards obtaining
their badges.

In the UK many of the stations taking part in the jamboree operate
with special GB call signs which are allocated for the period covering
the jamboree week.

UK amateur VHF band plans

50 MHz band

50·00–50·10	CW only
50·10–50·50	CW/SSB
50·50–52·00	All modes

70 MHz band

70·025–70·075	Beacons only
70·000–70·150	CW only
70·150–70·260	CW/SSB only
70·200	SSB call frequency
70·260–70·400	All modes
70·300	RTTY call frequency
70·350–70·400	Raynet
70·400–70·500	FM simplex only
70·450	FM call frequency

144 MHz band

144·00–144·15	CW only
144·15–144·50	CW/SSB only
144·80–144·84	All modes
144·84–145·00	Beacons
145·00–145·20	FM repeater inputs
145·20–145·60	FM simplex channels
145·60–145·80	FM repeater outputs
145·80–146·00	Satellite band

432 MHz band

430·00–432·00	Beacons only
432·00–432·15	CW only
432·15–432·50	CW/SSB only
432·50–432·80	All modes
432·80–433·00	Beacons
433·00–433·40	FM repeater outputs
433·40–434·60	FM simplex
434·60–435·00	FM repeater inputs
435·00–438·00	Satellite band
434·00–440·00	Amateur TV

1200 MHz band

1240·000–1256·000	Amateur TV (including RMT2/3 in)
1256·000–1260·000	All modes
1260·000–1270·000	Amateur satellite band
1270·000–1286·000	Amateur TV (including RMT1 in)
1286·000–1291·000	All modes
1291·000–1291·475	Repeater inputs (RM0–RM19)
1296·000–1296·025	Moonbounce (EME)
1296·025–1296·500	Narrow band DX operation
1296·500–1296·600	Linear transponder input
1296·600–1296·700	Linear transponder output
1296·800–1296·990	Beacons only
1297·000–1297·475	Repeater outputs (RM0–RM19)
1297·500–1298·000	Simplex channels (SM20–SM40)
1298·000–1300·000	All modes
1300·000–1325·000	TV repeater outputs (RMT1–RMT3)

Mobile and portable operation

The UK class A or B licence permits both mobile and portable
operation anywhere in Britain. When the station is operated from a
vehicle the suffix /M is added after the call sign (e.g. G3ABC/M). For
a station operated as a portable transmitter the suffix /P is added to
the call sign. If the station is set up at a temporary address different
from that listed on the licence the suffix /A is added to the call sign.

The call sign prefix is G for a station operating in England but
changes to GM (Scotland), GW (Wales), GI (Northern Ireland) etc.,
when the station operates from another part of Britain. Although the
prefix changes the rest of the call sign remains the same.

The ordinary class A or B licence may be used with a /M suffix for
operation from a boat on inland waterways or lakes but operation is
not permitted at sea or in a harbour or estuary. For true maritime
mobile operation at sea or in a harbour a separate licence is required.

The call sign used is the same as that allocated for the class A or B licence but during maritime mobile operation the suffix /MM is added to the call sign. The suffix /MA may be used when the boat or ship is anchored. For this type of operation from a commercial ship the permission of the master and owners of the ship must be obtained. In the case of a privately owned yacht or boat this is normally not a problem since the licensee is usually the owner.

Some countries permit operation from aircraft as an aeronautical mobile with the suffix /AM. This mode of operation is not permitted by the amateur radio licence in Britain.

FM simplex channels

On the 144 and 432 MHz bands a section of the band has been channelized for mobile radio use. For direct mobile to mobile contacts, known as simplex operation, the channels on 144 MHz occupy the frequency range from 145 200 to 145 575 kHz and are spaced at 25 kHz intervals with the channels labelled as S8 to S23 as follows:

Channel	Frequency (MHz)
S8	145·200
S9	145·225
S10	145·250
S11	145·275
S12	145·300
S13	145·325
S14	145·350
S15	145·375
S16	145·400
S17	145·425
S18	145·450
S19	145·475
S20	145·500
S21	145·525
S22	145·550
S23	145·575

Channel S12 is used for RTTY using AFSK.
Channel S20 is the FM calling channel
Channel S21 is used on Sundays for RSGB news broadcasts
Channel S22 is used for talk in at rallies

On the 432 MHz band the simplex channels are as follows:

Channel	Frequency (MHz)
SU12	433·300 MHz used for RTTY (AFSK)
SU16	433·400
SU17	433·425
SU18	433·450
SU19	433·475
SU20	433·500 FM calling channel
SU22	433·550 Talk in for rallies, etc.
SU24	433·600 RTTY (AFSK)
SU25–28	433·700–433·775 MHz used by RAYNET

On the 1·3 GHz band twenty-one simplex channels (SM20–SM40) have been allocated as follows:

Channel	Frequency (MHz)
SM20	1297·500
SM21	1297·525
SM22	1297·550
SM23	1297·575
SM24	1297·600
SM25	1297·625
SM26	1297·650
SM27	1297·675
SM28	1297·700
SM29	1297·725
SM30	1297·750
SM31	1297·775
SM32	1297·800
SM33	1297·825
SM34	1297·850
SM35	1297·875
SM36	1297·900
SM37	1297·925
SM38	1297·950
SM39	1297·975
SM40	1298·000

SM20 is used as the FM simplex calling channel.

FM repeaters

For mobile radio operation amateur clubs and groups have set up a number of repeater stations which permit the mobile station to achieve much greater coverage than by using simplex transmission. The repeater receives the signal from the mobile station on one frequency, known as the input frequency, and retransmits the same signal on a second frequency known as the output frequency. In Europe the input channel is generally 600 kHz below the output frequency for 144 MHz repeaters and 1600 kHz above the output frequency on 432 MHz repeaters.

In North America there are hundreds of repeaters and a range of input and output frequency differences may be encountered.

On 29 MHz FM repeaters operate on channels in the 29 500–29 700 band with an input to output frequency offset of 100 kHz. There are several 29 MHz repeaters in North America and some are being planned for the European area.

Access to most repeaters is achieved by sending a 500 mS tone burst with a frequency of 1750 Hz. Some repeaters are triggered by the presence of a carrier on the input frequency. Repeaters also have a timeout clock which switches the repeater to beacon mode about one to two minutes after it is accessed. This prevents the repeater being hogged by a user making excessively long transmissions.

144 MHz repeaters in Britain

Channel R0	Input 145·000	Output 145·600
	GB3CF Leicester	
	GB3EL East London	

Channel R1	Input 145·025	Output 145·625
	GB3AS Caldbeck, Cumbria	
	GB3NB Tacolneston, Norfolk	
	GB3SC Wimborne, Dorset	
	GB3WL West London	
Channel R2	Input 145·050	Output 145·650
	GB3HS Hull, Humberside	
	GB3MN Stockport, Cheshire	
	GB3SL South London	
	GB3TR Torquay, Devon	
Channel R3	Input 145·075	Output 145·675
	GB3MH Malvern, Worcestershire	
	GB3NA Barnsley, Yorkshire	
	GB3PO Martlesham, Suffolk	
	GB3PR Perth, Scotland	
	GB3SR Worthing, Sussex	
Channel R4	Input 145·100	Output 145·700
	GB3AR Bangor, Northern Ireland	
	GB3HH Buxton, Derbyshire	
	GB3HI Isle of Mull, Scotland	
	GB3KR Dover, Kent	
	GW3WH Abingdon, Oxfordshire	
Channel R5	Input 145·125	Output 145·725
	GB3BM Birmingham, West Midlands	
	GB3NC St Austell, Cornwall	
	GB3NI Belfast, Northern Ireland	
	GB3SN Fourmarks, Hampshire	
	GB3TW Tyne and Wear	
Channel R6	Input 145·150	Output 145·750
	GB3BC Mynnid Machen, Mid-Glamorgan	
	GB3CS Black Hill, Scotland	
	GB3MP Moel y Parc, Wales	
	GB3PI Barkway, Hertfordshire	
Channel R7	Input 145·175	Output 145·775
	GB3FR Old Bolingbroke, Lincolnshire	
	GB3GN Aberdeen, Scotland	
	GB3NL North London	
	GB3RF Burnley, Lancashire	
	GB3WT Armagh, Northern Ireland	
	GB3WW Carmel Dyfed, Wales	

432 MHz repeater channels

Channel	Input MHz	Output MHz
RB0	434·600	433·000
RB1	434·625	433·025
RB2	434·650	433·050
RB3	434·675	433·075
RB4	434·700	433·100
RB5	434·725	433·125
RB6	434·750	433·150
RB7	434·775	433·175
RB8	434·800	433·200
RB9	434·825	433·225
RB10	434·850	433·250
RB11	434·875	433·275

Channel	Input MHz	Output MHz
RB12	434·900	433·300
RB13	434·925	433·325
RB14	434·950	433·350
RB15	434·975	433·375

RB12 is used for RTTY repeaters using AFSK.

RB12 is used for RTTY repeaters using AFSK.

There are about 150 repeaters operating on these channels and serving local areas all over Britain. A full list of these repeaters together with their locations is available from the RSGB.

1·3 GHz repeater channels

Channel	Input MHz	Output MHz
RM0	1391·000	1397·000
RM1	1391·025	1397·025
RM2	1391·050	1397·050
RM3	1391·075	1397·075
RM4	1391·100	1397·100
RM5	1391·125	1397·125
RM6	1391·150	1397·150
RM7	1391·175	1397·175
RM8	1391·200	1397·200
RM9	1391·225	1397·225
RM10	1391·250	1397·250
RM11	1391·275	1397·275
RM12	1391·300	1397·300
RM13	1391·325	1397·325
RM14	1391·350	1397·350
RM15	1391·375	1397·375
RM16	1391·400	1397·400
RM17	1391·425	1397·425
RM18	1391·450	1397·450
RM19	1391·475	1397·475
RM20	1391·500	1397·500

Channel RM0	GB3AA Near Bristol, Avon
	GB3BH Watford, Hertfordshire
	GB3MC Bolton, Lancashire
Channel RM3	GB3CP Crawley, Sussex
	GB3PS Barkway, Hertfordshire
	GB3SE Stoke, Staffordshire
Channel RM6	GB3BW Brentwood, Essex
	GB3MM Wolverhampton, West Midlands
Channel RM9	GB3RU Reading, Berkshire
	GB3WX Brighton, Sussex
Channel RM15	GB3NL North London

SSB repeater

As an experiment a 144 MHz repeater using the SSB mode with a pilot tone has been set up. This is GB3SF which is located in Sheffield. The input signal must be transmitted with a small carrier level at about 16 dB below the PEP output level. The channel is provisionally designated as RS37 and the repeater output power is about 5 W PEP.

GB3SF   Input frequency 145·185 MHz
          Output frequency 145·785 MHz
          SSB with pilot tone at PEP − 16 dB

Linear transponder

This is a form of repeater which handles a whole band of frequencies unlike a conventional repeater which operates with just one channel. In the transponder the received signals in a band up to 100 kHz wide are mixed with a local oscillator and translated to a new band of frequencies which are then transmitted. This follows the same practice as that used for transponders on an amateur space satellite. Input and output signals are usually either CW or SSB and any number of contacts may take place simultaneously via the transponder. The transmitter power is shared among the various signals in the band in proportion to the received signals.

Currently two 100 kHz segments of the 1·3 GHz band are set aside for use by transponders with one segment (1296·5–1296·6) used as an input band and the other (1296·6–1296·7) as an output band.

Citizens band radio

In the UK two bands are allocated for citizens band (CB) radio operation and on both bands frequency modulation is used. The lower band is from 27·60125 MHz to 27·99125 MHz and contains forty channels. The upper band is from 934·025 MHz to 934·995 MHz and provides 20 channels. In general the UHF band tends to be used by semi-professional and business users while the lower band is used as a general communications band.

A licence for the use of a CB receiver or transmitter can be obtained from any Post Office.

UK 27 MHz CB channels

Channel	MHz	Channel	MHz
1	27·60125	21	27·80125
2	27·61125	22	27·81125
3	27·62125	23	27·82125
4	27·63125	24	27·83125
5	27·64125	25	27·84125
6	27·65125	26	27·85125
7	27·66125	27	27·86125
8	27·67125	28	27·87125
9	27·68125	29	27·88125
10	27·69125	30	27·89125
11	27·70125	31	27·90125
12	27·71125	32	27·91125

Channel	MHz	Channel	MHz
13	27·72125	33	27·92125
14	27·73125	34	27·93125
15	27·74125	35	27·94125
16	27·75125	36	27·95125
17	27·76125	37	27·96125
18	27·77125	38	27·97125
19	27·78125	39	27·98125
20	27·79125	40	27·99125

Channel 9 is reserved as an emergency channel and is monitored continuously by a series of volunteer stations. This is used for road traffic accidents and similar incidents where emergency help is required.

Channel 14 is used as a calling channel on which communication is first established before moving to another channel. Channel 19 is used as a calling channel by truck drivers following the practice in the USA where channel 19 is used as the calling channel.

Maximum output power:	4 W
Modulation:	FM (F3E) ± 2·5 kHz deviation
Antenna:	Single vertical wire or rod
Antenna length:	1·5 m maximum, including loading coil

27 MHz CB in Europe and the USA
During the high part of the sunspot cycle CB signals from the USA are often heard in Europe. These transmissions use amplitude modulation (A3E) or single sideband (J3E). Citizen band stations in continental Europe also use the US channel system with A3E or J3E transmissions. French CB stations use an FM (F3E) system similar to that in the UK.

USA 27 MHz CB channels

Channel	MHz	Channel	MHz
1	26·965	21	27·215
2	26·975	22	27·225
3	26·985	23	27·235
4	26·995	24	27·245
5	27·005	25	27·255
6	27·015	26	27·265
7	27·025	27	27·275
8	27·035	28	27·285
9	27·045	29	27·295
10	27·055	30	27·305
11	27·065	31	27·315
12	27·075	32	27·325
13	27·085	33	27·335
14	27·095	34	27·345
15	27·105	35	27·355
16	27·115	36	27·365
17	27·125	37	27·375
18	27·135	38	27·385
19	27·145	39	27·395
20	27·155	40	27·405

Note there are plans to allocate these channels for CB use in the UK with modified licence conditions compatible with the Committee of European Posts and Telecommunications (CEPT) regulations.

UK 934 MHz CB channels
In this band a total of twenty channels have currently been allocated at 50 kHz spacing as follows:

Channel	Frequency	Channel	Frequency
1	934·025 MHz	11	934·525 MHz
2	934·075 MHz	12	934·575 MHz
3	934·125 MHz	13	934·625 MHz
4	934·175 MHz	14	934·675 MHz
5	934·225 MHz	15	934·725 MHz
6	934·275 MHz	16	934·775 MHz
7	934·325 MHz	17	934·825 MHz
8	934·375 MHz	18	934·875 MHz
9	934·425 MHz	19	934·925 MHz
10	934·475 MHz	20	934·975 MHz

Maximum output power: 8 W
Modulation: FM (F3E) ± 5 kHz deviation
Antenna: Up to 12 element beams permitted
    Some other European countries also have a 934 MHz CB band.

3
Digital communication

Although the most familiar means of communication by radio are telephony and telegraphy using Morse code, an increasing amount of communications is conducted using digital techniques. In these systems each letter or figure in the message is converted into a stream of digital pulses. At the receiving end they are fed to a special printer or a visual display unit which converts the digital codes back into a display of printed text. The most familiar of these techniques is conventional radioteletype (RTTY) transmission which is used by both commercial and amateur stations. Various developments of RTTY such as TOR (teletype over radio), ARQ (automatic repeat request) and FEC (forward error control) have been introduced to reduce the errors when propagation conditions are difficult. The latest developments in this field include packet radio by which data is transmitted over a radio network in much the same fashion as it would be on a network of computer systems. We shall look at the technical characteristics of these digital transmission techniques.

Radio teletype

This method of digital transmission is based upon the commercial automatic radio telegraphy systems. The data for the text symbols is sent using an asynchronous serial code in which each letter or symbol is represented by a serial sequence of five pulses or bits. A single START bit at the space level is sent at the beginning of each character code to provide a timing reference which allows the receiver and transmitter circuits to be synchronized. After the character code there is a stop bit at the mark level for 1·5 bit times. The stop bit separates successive character codes so that the receiver can always detect the start bit of the next character code to maintain correct synchronization.

Baudot code

The code normally used for RTTY transmissions is the International Telecommunications Union (ITU) number 2 alphabet which is often referred to as Baudot code. Each data bit is allocated a time slot and if the bit is to be a 1 the signal is at mark while for a 0 state the signal is switched to the space condition. The data bits are sent with the least significant (bit 1) first (Figure 1).

The five-bit code allows thirty-two possible combinations which are not sufficient to handle both letters and figures so a shift system is used to switch between letters and figures. When figures are to be sent, a FIGS SHIFT code is transmitted and after this all codes are translated as figures or special signs. To return to the normal letters mode a LETTERS SHIFT code is sent (Figure 2). Only capital letters are available with this code. Certain control codes such as line feed, carriage return, space and the shift codes are common to both the letters and figures modes.

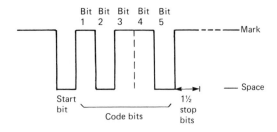

Figure 1 *The sequence of data signals for a single RTTY character using five bit Baudot code*

| LTRS | G | FIGS | 3 | LTRS | F | Z | X |

Figure 2 *Example of the use of FIGS and LTRS shift codes when sending a call sign via RTTY*

International Telecommunication Union number 2 code for RTTY (Baudot)

Code bits 54321	Hex value	Letters	Figures
00011	03	A	—
11001	19	B	?
01110	OE	C	:
01001	09	D	$
00001	01	E	3
01101	OD	F	!
11010	1A	G	&
10100	14	H	
00110	06	I	8
01011	OB	J	Bell
01111	OF	K	(
10010	12	L	)
11100	1C	M	.
01100	OC	N	,
11000	18	O	9
10110	16	P	0
10111	17	Q	1
01010	OA	R	4
00101	05	S	'
10000	10	T	5

Code	Hex value	Letters	Figures
00111	07	U	7
11110	1E	V	=
10011	13	W	2
11101	1D	X	/
10101	15	Y	6
10001	11	Z	+
01000	08	CR (carriage return)	
00010	02	LF (line feed)	
11111	1F	LTRS (letter shift)	
11011	1B	FIGS (figure shift)	
00100	04	SP (space)	
00000	00	BLK (blank)	

In the transmitted signal the binary bit pattern is used with a 0 bit corresponding to 'space' and a 1 bit representing a 'mark'. Data is transmitted with the least significant bit (bit 1) first.

Control sequences

Various symbol sequences are used by commercial telegraph operators to signify control actions. Some of these are also used by radio amateurs. Some popular codes are:

ZCZC	Start of message
NNNN	End of message
XXXXX	Error

SITOR and AMTOR

In the simple RTTY system there is no protection against errors caused by interference or fading where the data becomes corrupted. The SITOR (simplex teletype over radio) system developed for use in the commercial maritime radio service provides facilities for detecting and correcting errors in the received signal to give a more reliable RTTY type communications link. AMTOR (amateur teletype over radio) is the amateur radio version of the SITOR system of radioteletype transmission.

The SITOR coding system uses the same basic character set and shift modes as the conventional five-bit RTTY transmissions but each character code contains seven data bits instead of five. The seven-bit code allows up to 128 combinations but of these only thirty-five are actually used. The SITOR codes are chosen so that the bit pattern always contains four mark bits and three space bits. At the receiving end a simple check of the number of mark and space bits in the received code enables an error to be detected and action can be taken to correct the received data (Figure 3).

In SITOR there are no START or STOP bits and the blocks of seven data bits for each character code are sent one after another at a rate of 10 mS per bit (100 baud). This is a synchronous form of transmission system. As for conventional RTTY, the codes are sent with the least significant bit first. Synchronization is achieved by using certain special idling codes when no message data is being sent. Two different modes of operation are available in TOR type transmissions.

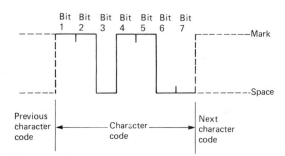

Figure 3   *The sequence of data signals for a single SITOR character code*

SITOR/AMTOR data code (CCIR 476)

Code word binary	Hex value	Letters	Figures
1000111	47	A	—
1110010	72	B	?
0011101	1D	C	:
1010011	53	D	$
1010110	56	E	3
0011011	1B	F	!
0110101	35	G	&
1101001	69	H	
1001101	4D	I	8
0010111	17	J	Bell
0011110	1E	K	(
1100101	65	L	)
0111001	39	M	.
1011001	59	N	,
1110001	71	O	9
0101101	2D	P	0
0101110	2E	Q	1
1010101	55	S	'
1110100	74	T	5
1001110	4E	U	7
0111100	3C	V	—
0100111	27	W	2
0111010	3A	X	/
0101011	2B	Y	6

Code word binary	Hex value	Letters	Figures
1100011	63	Z	+
1111000	78	CR (carriage return)	
1101100	6C	LF (line feed)	
1011010	5A	LTRS (letter shift)	
0110110	36	FIGS (figure shift)	
1011100	5C	SP (space)	
1101010	6A	BLK (blank)	
1100101	65	CS1 (control 1)	
1101010	6A	CS2 (control 2)	
1001101	4D	CS3 (control 3)	
0001111	0F	Idle (alpha)	
0110011	33	Idle (beta)	
1100110	66	Signal repetition	

Automatic repeat request mode

The usual mode of operation for AMTOR/SITOR stations is ARQ (automatic repeat request), which is also known as mode A. In this mode the transmitting station sends data in groups of three characters and after each group the receiving station replies with an acknowledgement signal which indicates whether the three character codes have been correctly received. The sequence is repeated every 450 mS. The three characters occupy 70 mS each giving a total of 210 mS of signal from the sending station. During the remaining 240 mS the receiving station sends back a single character code indicating the status of the received signals (Figure 4). Normally the receive station will send the CS1 and CS2 codes alternately. If an error is detected the receive station repeats the code that was sent for the previous block. When an error is signalled the transmitting station repeats the transmission of the last group of three character codes until reception is successfully acknowledged.

The ARQ mode is normally used for communication between two individual stations since it requires interaction between the two stations for proper operation. This type of operation is easily recognized by the regular chirp sound as the individual character groups are sent. There is also a noticeable change in the chirp sound when the station switches from sending three symbol groups to sending just the single character acknowledgement codes. Other stations may listen to a contact operating in this mode but the message may appear rather corrupted on the screen if there are errors and repetitions.

An important aspect of the ARQ mode is that the transmit-receive changeover operation at each station must be rapid otherwise the acknowledgement signal may be missed. This mode also presents problems on long distance contacts where the signal delay over the round trip path between the stations may exceed the available time in which the acknowledgement must be received.

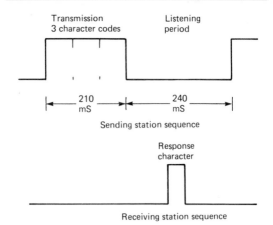

Figure 4 *The timing sequence for the sending and receiving stations in AMTOR ARQ mode*

Automatic repeat request calling sequence

In this mode the station which starts the contact becomes the master and controls the timing sequence of the signals. The calling sequence consists of two three character blocks which may be repeated until a contact is established. In the first block the second character is a signal repetition (RQ) and in the second block the third character is an RQ code. The other characters in the two blocks are normal character codes which may represent the call sign of the calling station. To establish contact the receiving station responds with alternate CS1 and CS2 codes. On receipt of two successive CS1 (or CS2) codes the transmitting station starts to send the message (Figure 5).

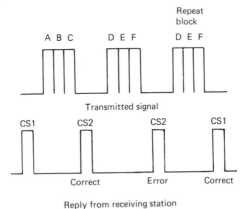

Figure 5 *Example of the repetition sequence used for correcting errors in the ARQ mode*

ARQ changeover sequence

To change the direction of data flow the sending station transmits the sequence (FIGS SHIFT + ?). On receipt of this the receiving station sends a CS3 code as its response. When the sending station detects the CS3 code it transmits the sequence (beta, alpha, beta). On receipt of this sequence the receiving station changes to the transmit mode and sends a block of three RQ codes if it is a slave station. If the receiving station is a master this block contains one RQ and two other characters. When the sending station detects the RQ code it switches to receive and changeover is complete.

If the receiving station wishes to change to send mode it transmits a CS3 code in response to a received block. On receipt of the CS3 code the sending station transmits the sequence (beta, alpha, beta) and the changeover occurs as before.

ARQ contact termination

The sending station may terminate a contact by sending the 'end of communication' sequence (alpha, alpha, alpha). If a receiving station wishes to terminate the contact it must first initiate a changeover so that it becomes the sending station and then it transmits the end of communication sequence (alpha, alpha, alpha). Communication may also be terminated if continuous errors occur in sixty-four successive blocks of data.

FEC broadcast mode

The alternative mode of operation for AMTOR/SITOR is FEC (forward error control) or, more simply, mode B. In the FEC mode the transmitting station sends the message twice with the repeat version interleaved with the original message sequence. The primary message is sent using the odd numbered symbol slots in the message stream. The repeated message is sent in the even numbered slots but is delayed five words behind the main message (Figure 6).

At the start of transmission both the message slots and the repeat slots are filled with idle characters to allow the receiving station to synchronize its decoding circuits. Here the message slots contain a CS1 code and the repeat slots contain a CS2 code to allow the receiving stations to synchronize correctly. This idling pattern is also sent between messages to maintain synchronism.

The advantage of this mode is that it does not require an acknowledgement signal from the receiving station and may be correctly decoded by several stations. This mode is suited for broadcast transmissions, such as CQ calls (general calls to all stations), which are intended for reception by a number of receiving stations. The FEC broadcast mode is generally used for amateur news transmissions and propagation forecasts. In amateur contacts the FEC mode may be used for the initial call and when contact has been established the two stations generally switch to the ARQ mode. The FEC mode has the advantage that it is not affected by transmit–receive changeover delays or propagation delays between two distant stations which can present problems when the ARQ mode is used.

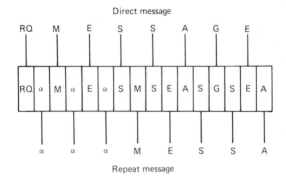

Figure 6   *The character transmission sequence for a message in the AMTOR FEC broadcast mode*

FEC selective mode

There is an alternative mode of operation for FEC known as the selective mode. This is used in the maritime mobile service for messages intended for a specific station. In this selective mode the initial phasing sequence is sent normally, the call sign of the receiving station and the following messages are transmitted with the data signals inverted so that each code contains three 'mark' bits and four 'space' bits. On receipt of its call sign the receiving station automatically inverts the received data to reproduce the correct message information. During the time between messages the 'idle beta' signal is sent. This mode is not normally used by amateur stations.

FEC error detection

At the receiving end both the initial and repeated codes are checked for possible errors. If the initial code is correct it is printed. If an error is detected the repeat code is checked and if correct is printed. If both codes contain an error a space is printed. The repetition sequence effectively provides time diversity and in general if the code in one copy of the message is affected by interference or fading the code in the repeated message is likely to be received correctly so that under most conditions the message is printed correctly at the receiving end.

ASCII coded RTTY

Some amateur stations use the eight-bit ASCII (American standard code for information interchange) code when transmitting RTTY. This code is widely used to represent text in home computer systems and for communications between computers. This code may also be used by amateur stations when sending computer programs to one another. The international version of the ASCII code is known as ISO7 and includes some variations to allow special symbols, such as the £ sign, to be included for other countries.

Unlike the ITU number 2 code, ASCII provides seven bits for the character code. This allows up to 128 different combinations for upper and lower case letters and a range of other symbols without the need for shift codes. The eighth bit in the transmitted code is used as an error check. This bit may be set at either 1 or 0 to make the total number of 1 bits in the character code an odd number (Figure 7). At the receiving end the number of 1 bits is checked and if it is odd then the received character is correct, otherwise an error has occurred and some action may be taken to deal with this if desired. The error check or parity bit may also be arranged to operate with an even number of 1 bits if desired.

The first thirty-two codes in the set are reserved as control codes providing such functions as line feed, carriage return, bell etc.

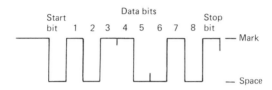

Figure 7   *The sequence of data signals for a single RTTY character using the ASCII code*

ASCII code table

Decimal	Hex	Binary	Symbol
0	00	0000000	NUL
1	01	0000001	SOH
2	02	0000010	STX
3	03	0000011	ETX
4	04	0000100	EOT
5	05	0000101	ENQ
6	06	0000110	ACK
7	07	0000111	BRL
8	08	0001000	BS
9	09	0001001	HT
10	0A	0001010	LF
11	0B	0001011	VT
12	0C	0001100	FF
13	0D	0001101	CR
14	0E	0001110	SO
15	0F	0001111	SI
16	10	0010000	DLE
17	11	0010001	DC1
18	12	0010010	DC2
19	13	0010011	DC3
20	14	0010100	DC4
21	15	0010101	NAK
22	16	0010110	SYN
23	17	0010111	ETB
24	18	0011000	CAN
25	19	0011001	EM
26	1A	0011010	SUB
27	1B	0011011	ESC
28	1C	0011100	FS
29	1D	0011101	GS
30	1E	0011110	RS

Decimal	Hex	Binary	Symbol
31	1F	0011111	US
32	20	0100000	Space
33	21	0100001	!
34	22	0100010	'
35	23	0100011	£ or #
36	24	0100100	$
37	25	0100101	%
38	26	0100110	&
39	27	0100111	'
40	28	0101000	(
41	29	0101001	)
42	2A	0101010	*
43	2B	0101011	+
44	2C	0101100	,
45	2D	0101101	—
46	2E	0101110	.
47	2F	0101111	/
48	30	0110000	0
49	31	0110001	1
50	32	0110010	2
51	33	0110011	3
52	34	0110100	4
53	35	0110101	5
54	36	0110110	6
55	37	0110111	7
56	38	0111000	8
57	39	0111001	9
58	3A	0111010	:
59	3B	0111011	;
60	3C	0111100	<
61	3D	0111101	=
62	3E	0111110	>
63	3F	0111111	?
64	40	1000000	@
65	41	1000001	A
66	42	1000010	B
67	43	1000011	C
68	44	1000100	D
69	45	1000101	E
70	46	1000110	F
71	47	1000111	G
72	48	1001000	H
73	49	1001001	I
74	4A	1001010	J
75	4B	1001011	K
76	4C	1001100	L
77	4D	1001101	M
78	4E	1001110	N
79	4F	1001111	O
80	50	1010000	P
81	51	1010001	Q
82	52	1010010	R
83	53	1010011	S
84	54	1010100	T
85	55	1010101	U
86	56	1010110	V
87	57	1010111	W
88	58	1011000	X
89	59	1011001	Y
90	5A	1011010	Z
91	5B	1011011	[
92	5C	1011100	\
93	5D	1011101	]

Decimal	Hex	Binary	Symbol
94	5E	1011110	ˆ
95	5F	1011111	–
96	60	1100000	'
97	61	1100001	a
98	62	1100010	b
99	63	1100011	c
100	64	1100100	d
101	65	1100101	e
102	66	1100110	f
103	67	1100111	g
104	68	1101000	h
105	69	1101001	i
106	6A	1101010	j
107	6B	1101011	k
108	6C	1101100	l
109	6D	1101101	m
110	6E	1101110	n
111	6F	1101111	o
112	70	1110000	p
113	71	1110001	q
114	72	1110010	r
115	73	1110011	s
116	74	1110100	t
117	75	1110101	u
118	76	1110110	v
119	77	1110111	w
120	78	1111000	x
121	79	1111001	y
122	7A	1111010	z
123	7B	1111011	{
124	7C	1111100		
125	7D	1111101	}
126	7E	1111110	~
127	7F	1111111	DEL

Control code functions

ACK	Acknowledge
	Block received OK
BS	Backspace
	Go back one character space
CAN	Cancel
	Cancel line (i.e. all back to last CR)
CR	Carriage return
	Return to start of line
DC1–4	Device control codes
DEL	Delete (erase previous symbol)
DLE	Data link escape
	Changes meaning of following two or three codes
EM	End of medium
ENQ	Enquiry
	Requests response from remote station
EOT	End of transmission
ESC	Escape
	Selects alternative meaning for following symbol codes

ETB	End of transmission block
	Indicates end of a block of data or text
ETX	End of text
	Terminates text
FF	Form feed (new page)
FS	File separator
GS	Group separator
HT	Horizontal tab
LF	Line feed
	Move down one line
NAK	Negative acknowledge
	Used to indicate an error in reception
NUL	Null
RS	Record separator
SI	Shift in
	Select normal character set
SO	Shift out
	Select alternative character set
SOH	Start of header
	Indicates start of header section of frame
STX	Start of text
	Indicates start of message section of frame
SUB	Substitute
	Replace previous character
SYN	Synchronization idle pattern
US	Unit separator
VT	Vertical tab

Baud rates

The rate of transmission of digital signals is normally measured as a baud rate and for binary coded transmissions this rate is given by the number of bits transmitted per second. Thus a transmission in which bits are sent at a rate of 50 per second would be referred to as a 50 baud transmission. In an asynchronous transmission such as standard RTTY the baud rate is determined by the rate at which bits are sent when a character code is transmitted and does not represent the overall rate at which data is being sent since there may be periods between character codes where no data is actually being sent and the signal is simply held at the mark level.

For amateur transmissions the baud rate is usually 45, 50 or 75 baud for standard RTTY. Commercial RTTY stations generally use 50 baud or 75 baud. When ASCII coded signals are sent the baud rate may be increased to 110 baud on the HF bands. For SITOR/AMTOR transmissions 100 baud is always used. Packet radio generally uses 300 baud for the HF bands and 1200 baud for VHF and UHF transmissions but baud rates up to 9600 have also been used.

The time period for each data bit for the various transmission speeds is as follows:

Baud rate	Pulse width mS
45	22
50	20
75	13·3
100	10
110	9
150	6·7
300	3·3
1200	0·8
2400	0·4

RTTY transmission techniques

Although the digital codes consist simply of on/off pulse signals the data is normally transmitted by using frequency modulation techniques. On the HF bands two frequencies at a spacing of a few hundred hertz are used to represent the mark and space conditions of the signals. Thus the transmitter radiates a constant power carrier and simply shifts the frequency in sympathy with the code signals. This technique is known as frequency shift keying (FSK).

The amount of frequency shift used varies according to the service in which the RTTY signal is used as follows:

Shift Hz	Service
850 Hz	RTTY (weather, amateur, military)
425 Hz	RTTY (press, amateur, commercial)
170 Hz	RTTY (amateur), AMTOR, SITOR

On the HF bands the mark and space conditions are produced by simply shifting the carrier frequency. This is known as frequency shift keying (FSK) and has the emission designation F1B. Amateur stations generally use a frequency shift of 170 Hz for RTTY. The normal carrier frequency is used to represent 'mark' and the frequency is shifted 170 Hz lower for 'space'. The wider 425 Hz or 850 Hz frequency shifts are used by some amateurs to give a lower error rate and easier tuning. Commercial and military stations use either 425 or 850 Hz shift for RTTY and 170 Hz for SITOR. Some commercial stations use reverse shift so that the space frequency is higher than the normal carrier frequency.

In most amateur stations the frequency shift is achieved by switching a pair of audio tone signals to a conventional SSB transmitter where one tone represents mark and the other space. The tuning is then offset so that the mark tone produces the nominal carrier frequency. The two commonly used tones in Europe are 1275 Hz and 1445 Hz to give 170 Hz shift. The higher tone is the mark frequency. For 425 Hz and 850 Hz shifts the mark tone becomes 1700 Hz or 2125 Hz. Other parts of the world use higher frequency tone pairs with a mark tone of 2125 Hz and space tones of 2295, 2550 or 2975 Hz. Here the space tone is the higher frequency of the pair. Most modern RTTY terminal units have a simple facility for switching the sense of the tones if required.

An important aspect to consider when operating a conventional SSB transceiver in this mode is that the power stages of amateur transceivers are often designed to handle full output power only on an intermittent basis as would be the case for normal telephony. When FSK RTTY signals are generated the full power is output continuously and for most transceivers it will be necessary to reduce the output power level to perhaps 50 per cent of the maximum rating of the transmitter to avoid overheating. The latest models however are generally designed to handle continuous full power carrier output for use in the FSK mode.

On VHF and UHF a modified technique known as audio frequency shift keying (AFSK) is used. In this case two audio tones are used to represent the mark and space conditions and the resultant audio signal is then used to modulate the transmitter carrier using narrow band frequency modulation. The frequency shift used is generally either 170 Hz or 425 Hz with the space tone set at 1275 Hz and the mark tone at either 1445 Hz or 1700 Hz. VHF transmissions using conventional FSK may also be used.

For reception the two tone audio signal is passed to some form of frequency discriminator which extracts the mark and space digital signals from the switched audio tones. Another approach uses narrowband audio filters to select the two tones. The filter outputs are then amplified and rectified and fed to opposite inputs of a comparator which then outputs the required logic signals. Alternative techniques use a phase locked oscillator from which the control signal is used to produce the digital signal. Some personal computers, such as the Apple and Spectrum can be used to decode RTTY purely by software. This involves using the computer to measure the period of the audio tone input and from this to generate the bit states for decoding into the appropriate character information.

Where to find amateur RTTY

Frequencies generally used for amateur RTTY are as follows:

3·5 MHz band	3580–3620 kHz
7 MHz band	7035–7045 kHz
14 MHz band	14 080–14 110 kHz RTTY
	14 075–14 080 kHz AMTOR
21 MHz band	21 080–21 120 kHz
28 MHz band	28 050–28 150 kHz
144 MHz band	144·600 MHz (FSK)
	145·300 MHz (AFSK)
430 MHz band	432·600 MHz (FSK)
	433·300 MHz (AFSK)

For the frequencies of commercial RTTY stations see the section on utility stations.

Bulletin boards

One application of RTTY type transmissions is the provision of automatic stations which act as mailboxes or bulletin boards. Here the bulletin board is usually controlled by a home computer. To log in to the bulletin board the amateur station usually has to send its call sign and carriage return/line feed when requested by the bulletin board. On receipt of this signal the bulletin board responds by acknowledging the station call and giving instructions on the commands for operating the bulletin board. Most boards will provide a list of messages currently on file and may also give a log of stations that have accessed the board during the previous twenty-four hours. The amateur station may send a message to be stored and forwarded by the board or for general display to any amateur accessing the board. Some bulletin boards provide other facilities such as conversion of locator codes, details of the station equipment and perhaps simple computer programs which can be run by sending appropriate commands.

Currently there are a number of mailbox or bulletin boards operating on the HF and VHF bands. On HF most boards can operate with RTTY at either 45 or 75 baud using the ITU2 alphabet but some use the AMTOR system. Examples of these are:

EA7AHL	14 094 kHz (RTTY)
EA7BTQ	14 087 kHz (RTTY)
DJ3YV/EA8	14 078 kHz (AMTOR)
G3PLX	3587 kHz (AMTOR)
HB9EP	3580 kHz (RTTY)

Packet radio

The latest form of digital communications now being used by amateurs is packet radio. The system effectively sets up a communications network between several stations. Each station may send packets or frames of data over the link and these may be addressed to a specific station or broadcast generally on the network. The system used is a variation of the X25 data link protocol which is called AX25. Packet radio uses synchronous transmission where character codes are sent one after another with no start or stop bits. A special flag character is sent at the start of the data block to provide a timing reference from which the timing of all other data within the block may be derived. The eight-bit ASCII character code is used. Each frame consists of a series of 'fields' which may contain one or more eight bit data codes.

The system is designed to operate as a network so that stations may simply receive frames and then forward them on to another station in the chain until eventually the frame reaches the destination station. The linking stations may be digital repeaters or forwarding may be done via another amateur station. In a complete message sent via a network of stations some frames may travel along different routes between the source and destination stations. In the header section of the frame a serial code indicates the order in which the received frames should be reassembled to reproduce the complete message.

The basic frame format for amateur AX25 signals consists of a flag field, an address field, a control field, the main data block, an error check field and a final flag to indicate the end of the frame (Figure 8).

Start flag	Address field	Control field	Information (text) field	F C S	End flag
1 byte	14 – 70 bytes	1 byte	Up to 256 bytes	2 bytes	1 byte

Figure 8   *Basic format for a frame of information in the packet radio system*

Flag fields
The starting and ending flag fields have the unique data pattern 01111110. The start flag is used for synchronization and defines the point from which the timing of all following data words is derived. To avoid this pattern occurring in other fields the transmitter automatically inserts a 0 bit after any string of five 1 bits. This is known as *bit stuffing* and these extra 0 bits are removed automatically at the receiver end.

Address field
This field contains fourteen to seventy bytes of address information arranged in groups of seven bytes each. In each group the first six bytes hold the station call sign in upper case letters and figures and the seventh byte is a secondary station identifier (SSI) used to differentiate between stations, such as digipeaters and bulletin boards, which may use the same call sign. The first group identifies the station to which the message is being sent while the second group identifies the source station which is sending the message. If the message is to be routed via digipeaters up to eight further groups of seven bytes may be added to identify the stations through which the message is to be passed (Figure 9).

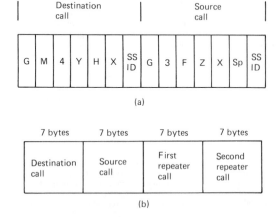

(a)

(b)

Figure 9   *The packet radio address field formats:*
(a) For simple two station contacts;
(b) For contacts via repeaters

Control field

The control field consists of one byte which indicates the type of
frame being sent. The three types of frame are *information* (I),
supervisory (S) and *unnumbered* (U) (Figure 10).

For I frames the control field contains two three-bit sequence
numbers which are used to keep track of which frames have been
transmitted and successfully received.

Supervisory frames are used to acknowledge receipt of I frames or
to request retransmission. Bits 2 and 3 of the control field indicate the
action required and the sequence number indicates the last frame
number that was successfully received.

Unnumbered frames are used for various control functions. Bits 2,
3, 5, 6 and 7 of the control field in these frames are used to indicate the
type of action required. *Unnumbered information* (UI) frames may be
used for net or round table operation but errors in received data do
not cause retransmission of frames.

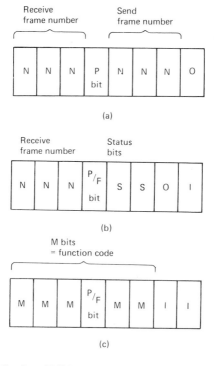

Figure 10   *Control field formats for packet radio:*
(a) *Information (I) frame;*
(b) *Supervisory (S) frame;*
(c) *Unnumbered (U) frame*

Information field

The information field contains the message that is being sent and may be up to 256 bytes in length. This field may also contain control information in the first few bytes which indicates the type of network protocol that is in use.

Frame check sequence

The *frame check sequence* (FCS) is a sixteen-bit word which provides an error check on the data sent within the frame. The transmitted FCS word is calculated from the data sent in the transmitted frame. At the receiving end a similar FCS word is calculated from the received data and if this matches the received FCS then the data is correct and is accepted.

AX25 protocol specification

For more details of the full AX25 protocol used for packet radio readers should consult *The AX25 Specification* published by the Amateur Radio Relay League and available in Britain from the Radio Society of Great Britain.

Transmission technique

At each station the encoding and decoding of frames and their assembly or disassembly to provide messages is controlled by a small computer called a *terminal node controller* (TNC). In most cases this is a dedicated microprocessor based device but it would also be possible to use a personal computer to perform this function provided it were fitted with a suitable serial interface capable of handling the high level data link control type of data link protocol.

Transmission uses FSK or AFSK with a shift of 200 Hz for HF bands and 1000 Hz for the VHF bands. Data is usually converted into the *non return to zero space* (NRZ-S) format before transmission (Figure 11). In this scheme a zero in the data bit pattern causes a change in output frequency whilst a one bit causes no change.

Packet radio activity on HF can be found around 14103 MHz.

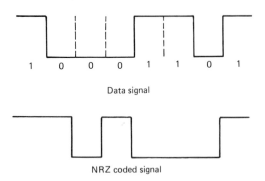

Data signal

NRZ coded signal

Figure 11   *NRZ signal format used for transmission in packet radio*

Digipeaters

For packet radio operation a *digital repeater* (digipeater) may be used to link two distant stations on VHF or UHF. Most digipeaters transmit and receive on the same frequency. The received frame of data is temporarily stored in a memory and then relayed to the destination station or the next digipeater in the chain.

In Britain, an experimental network of digipeaters has been set up. These digipeaters normally operate on 144·650 MHz but there is an option to use an alternative frequency of 145·275 MHz to permit duplex operation.

Digipeaters in Britain

Call	Location	Polarization
GB3AP	Dudley, West Midlands	V
GB3BP	Bristol, Avon	V
GB3CD	Crewe, Cheshire	V
GB3DB	Honiton, Devon	V
GB3DC	Weymouth, Dorset	V
GB3EP	Exeter, Devon	V
GB3HP	Winchester, Hampshire	V
GB3HQ	Potters Bar, Hertfordshire	H
GB3JP	Jersey, Channel Islands	V
GB3KP	Kingston, Surrey	H
GB3NP	Norwich, Norfolk	V
GB3UP	Guildford, Surrey	H
GB3XP	New Malden, Surrey	H
GB3YP	Harrogate, North Yorkshire	V

Gateways and teleports

A mode of operation which may be used in packet radio is the gateway or teleport system. This is a form of repeater which can send the packet signal via an amateur satellite to another ground terminal and thence to an amateur station at a remote location. Some satellites are equipped with store and forward facilities operating on much the same lines as a ground based digipeater. The possibilities of packet radio as a communications medium are extensive and many avenues are being explored for possible future use.

4

Picture communication

Facsimile (fax)

Facsimile is a method of transmission of pictures as a narrow band signal which is generally used for weather charts, press photos and for amateur picture communication. The system is similar in many ways to slow scan television but has a higher picture resolution and a much slower transmission rate. Typically a picture will take about twenty minutes for transmission. There are no line sync pulses and the system relies upon the receiver display device having the correct scanning speed. Timing and synchronization signals are sent at the start of the picture transmission and these signals also identify the format of the picture being sent.

At the transmitting end the picture or chart is wrapped around a rotating drum (Figure 12). A lamp and photocell sensor on a movable head detects the image density as the drum rotates and this effectively scans one line across the chart. After each drum revolution the pickup head is moved axially a short distance along the drum to scan a new line adjacent to the first. This continues until the whole picture or chart has been scanned. At the receiving end a similar drum system is used but in this case the head carries a light source whose intensity can be varied in sympathy with the received signal. The paper used is light sensitive and produces a copy of the original image as the scanning process is carried out. Fax pictures may also be produced by using a personal computer system and a dot matrix type printer.

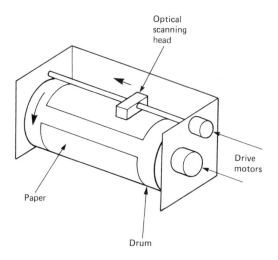

Figure 12   *Basic arrangement of a facsimile (fAX) machine*

Index of cooperation (IOC)

This defines the aspect ratio (width to height) of the picture and is given by

IOC = drum diameter × line density

Usual values for IOC are 288 and 576.

Line density

This is the number of lines per millimetre on the paper. Usual values are 1·9 lines/mm (IOC = 288) and 3·8 lines/mm (IOC = 576) based on a drum diameter of 152 mm. American machines will usually have the density specified in lines per inch and the drum diameter in inches.

Lines per minute

This is determined by the rotation speed of the scanning drum. The rates normally used are 60, 90, 120 or 240 lines per minute. The drum rotates once for each scan line.

Transmission format

The transmission format is defined by the number of lines per minute and the IOC in use. It is usually shown in the form l.p.m./IOC. Thus a format of 120/288 means 120 lines per minute with an IOC of 288.

Modulation scheme

On HF, FAX signals use frequency modulation (F3C). For black and white charts the frequency shift is:

Black level $f_0 - 400$ Hz
White level $f_0 + 400$ Hz

For photographs grey levels produce frequencies between these limits.

Reception on the HF bands can be achieved by using the SSB receive mode and offsetting the tuning to give a tone which shifts between 1500 Hz for black and 2300 Hz for white. The frequency modulated tone is then demodulated to give the required brightness signal for the recorder.

Mode identifier tones

The IOC in use is indicated by a sequence of alternating black and white signals at the start of transmission of a picture. The frequency of the black/white pulses is 300 Hz for an IOC of 576 and 675 Hz for an IOC of 288. On receipt of these signals the facsimile machine automatically selects the required IOC.

Phasing signal

At the start of picture transmission an alternating black and white signal is used to define the start point of the scanning lines so that the receiving scanner can synchronize to the received signal (Figure 13). One black/white cycle occurs per scan line with one half of the line black and the other half white. Some systems use a phasing signal which is 95 per cent black with a 5 per cent white pulse. The start of the line is indicated by the start of the white part of the phasing signal.

Transmission time

The time taken to send a complete picture depends upon the combination of the number of lines per minute, the IOC and the physical size of the picture being transmitted. Typical transmission times for weather charts are:

Lines/ minute	IOC	Time (seconds)
60	288	18·8
90	288	12·5
90	576	25·0
120	288	9·4
120	576	18·8
240	288	4·7
240	576	9·4

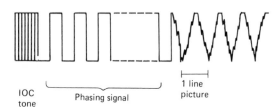

IOC tone

Phasing signal

1 line picture

Figure 13   *Typical signal format at the start of the transmission of a fAX picture*

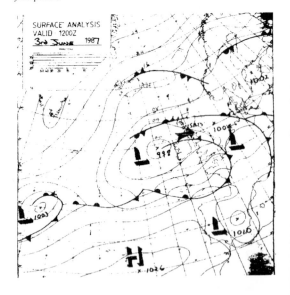

Figure 14   *An example of a fAX picture produced using an Apple II computer and dot matrix printer*

Amateur facsimile

Amateur facsimile generally uses the 120/288 format and may sometimes be found on HF around the following frequencies.

3600 kHz
7040 kHz
14 100 kHz (Europe)
14 245 kHz (USA)

There is a European facsimile net which meets on 14 100 kHz most days at around 1700 GMT and a news broadcast is made on Saturdays on 3600 kHz at 1700 GMT and on Sundays at 1000 GMT on about 14 102 kHz.

Slow scan television

Slow scan television (SSTV) is a system for transmitting pictures via an HF channel using the normal audio frequency bandwidth. This is achieved by reducing the scanning rate until the video frequency signals representing the picture information will fit into the audio bandwidth of 2·5 kHz approximately. A number of different standards are currently in use but the most popular uses a picture made up of 120 or 128 lines. In computer generated displays there are usually 128 picture elements (pixels) per line.

The original standard used 120 scan lines with different timings for the USA and Europe because their frame rates are based on local mains frequencies.

	Europe	USA
Line scan period mS	60	66
Frame scan period s	7·2	8·0

The signals for SSTV are used to frequency modulate an audio frequency carrier to give an audio frequency of 1200 Hz for the tip of the sync pulses, 1500 Hz for black level and 2300 Hz for peak white (Figure 15).

For standard format signals each scan line is 67 mS in duration and the line sync pulse is 5 mS long. A complete frame of 128 lines takes approximately 8 s to transmit and at the end of the frame a field sync pulse of 30 mS duration is transmitted.

Alternative modes of transmission to give better resolution but slower transmission times are:

16 second frame 128 lines at 133 mS 128 × 256 pixels
32 second frame 256 lines at 133 mS 256 × 256 pixels

Colour pictures can be transmitted by sending three separate pictures in succession taken through red, green and blue filters respectively. At the receiving end each picture is stored separately in memory and the three are combined to provide a composite colour signal for a monitor or colour TV receiver. An alternative

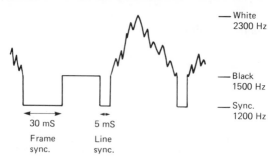

Figure 15 *Basic waveform and timing for an SSTV signal*

Figure 16 *Example of an SSTV picture received using a computer for decoding and display*

transmission mode uses line sequential colour in which each line is scanned sequentially in red, green and blue so that the three colour frames are interleaved during transmission.

Some colour standards are:

24 second mode 128 lines at 67 mS
48 second mode 128 lines at 133 mS
96 second mode 256 lines at 133 mS

Another colour mode which has been seen from some stations in the USA uses a multiplexed component scheme similar to the multiplexed analogue components (MAC) system for high definition colour transmission. This appears to have luminance on one scan line and the two colour difference signals time compressed to fit into the two halves of the following scan line.

Slow scan signals can be found around the following frequencies in the amateur bands:

3·5 MHz   3735–3745 kHz
7 MHz   7035–7045 kHz

14 MHz	14 225–14 235 kHz
	14 170 kHz
21 MHz	21 335–21 345 kHz
28 MHz	28 675–28 775 kHz
144 MHz	144 500 kHz
432 MHz	432 500 kHz

Fast scan television

Amateur transmissions of conventional high definition television both in monochrome and in colour may be found in the 430 MHz and 1200 MHz bands and also in the higher bands such as 2300 MHz. Transmissions usually follow the same standard as that used in the country of operation, so in Britain the 625 line 50 fields per second standard would be used with PAL encoding for colour transmissions.

On 420 MHz the transmission method uses amplitude modulation with one sideband filtered out (C3F) (Figure 17). Sound is generally transmitted on a separate channel often on 144 MHz but some transmissions may use intercarrier sound.

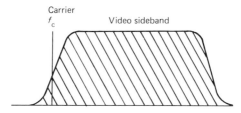

Figure 17 *Spectrum of the vestigial sideband signal (C3F) used for amateur UHF fast scan television*

Fast scan television on the 432 MHz band is generally confined to the upper end of the band from 334–340 MHz which is also shared with the amateur satellite service. ATV operation is normally arranged to avoid causing interference to other users of this part of the 432 MHz band. In most cases only the vision signal is transmitted at 432 MHz but a sound link for talk back is usually established on the 144 MHz which allows the receiving station to report on the quality of the received pictures and the transmitting station to comment on what is being transmitted on the vision channel. The generally used frequency for ATV talk back is 144·750 MHz and this channel is also used to establish communications before a television transmission is attempted.

When the 1300 MHz band is used for fast scan television transmissions either AM (C3F) or FM (F3F) may be used for the vision signal (Figure 17). The voice signal may be transmitted using FM (F3E) at a frequency 6 MHz above the vision carrier. For AM video transmission this may be a 6 MHz subcarrier. Colour transmissions are made using the PAL system with chrominance information transmitted on a subcarrier of 4·33 MHz. Colour cameras are now readily available for use with home video recorders and a suitable video signal for the transmitter is generally available from a video recorder. Previously recorded material may be sent by using the playback signal from a video recorder to drive the vision transmitter. Amateur stations are not permitted to broadcast entertainment programmes so any prerecorded material used consists of amateur videos of family or radio club activities and local events.

FM television

Although normal fast scan TV signals use amplitude modulation for the video component an alternative approach is to use frequency modulation for the video signal. This takes up a wider bandwidth but provides some advantages and is now used by amateurs for transmissions on the 1200 and 2300 MHz bands. This mode of transmission is generally used for commercial satellite television transmissions.

Television repeaters

In the UK several amateur repeaters have been set up for fast scan television signals. These operate in the 1200 MHz and 2300 MHz bands using the following channels:

Television repeater channels (UK)

RMT1   Input 1276·5 MHz   Output 1311·5 MHz
RMT2   Input 1249·0 MHz   Output 1318·5 MHz
RMT3   Input 1248·0 MHz   Output 1308·0 MHz

British television repeaters

Call	Location	Channel	Video
GB3AF	Durham	RMT2	
GB3CT	Crawley, Surrey	RMT2	FM
GB3GT	Glasgow	RMT2	FM
GB3GV	Leicester, Leicestershire	RMT2	
GB3HV	High Wycombe, Bucks	RMT3	
GB3PV	Cambridge, Cambridgeshire	RMT2	FM
GB3TV	Dunstable, Bedfordshire	RMT2	
GB3UD	Stoke on Trent, Staffordshire	RMT2	
GB3UT	Bath, Avon	RNT1	
GB3VI	Hastings, East Sussex	RMT1	AM
GB3VR	Brighton, West Sussex	RMT2	FM

Picture quality report code

P1   Barely visible
P2   Poor
P3   Fair
P4   Good
P5   Excellent

5
Utility stations

Apart from broadcasting and amateur radio stations most of the signals on the HF, VHF and UHF bands provide special services and are generally referred to as utility stations. Many of these provide communications for government, commercial and military purposes using a variety of transmission modes. Some of these signals will be scrambled or enciphered to provide privacy and security.

It should be noted that these stations are not intended for public broadcasting and their reception is not covered by the normal radio receiving licences. Listeners are reminded that the divulgence or improper use of any information gained from these transmissions constitutes a violation of the international telecommunications laws and is a criminal offence in most countries.

Utility stations can provide useful test signals for checking RTTY and facsimile equipment since unlike amateur stations they usually operate to some form of schedule and transmit for long periods. The signals from these stations are also a useful guide to propagation conditions since in general they produce stronger and more consistent signals than amateur stations.

Press stations

A number of press agency stations broadcast news on the HF bands. Most of these use the 50 baud RTTY mode of transmission with the ITU number 2 alphabet. Frequency shift is usually 425 Hz with the higher frequency being a 'mark'. A few stations use 75 or 100 baud transmissions and some operate with reversed frequency shift. Transmissions may be in a variety of languages such as English, French, German and Spanish. Transmissions in Russian and Arabic use special versions of the ITU code and are not readily deciphered. The bands where these stations are to be found are:

5200–5500 kHz
5800–6000 kHz
6900–7000 kHz
7400–8200 kHz
8900–9500 kHz
9800–10 000 kHz
10 500–11 200
11 400–11 600 kHz
13 400–13 800 kHz
14 350–15 000 kHz
15 500–16 500 kHz
18 200–18 700 kHz
20 200–20 500 kHz

Some typical frequencies are:

TASS, Moscow	5830, 6950, 8140, 10 465, 14 490 kHz
USIA, New York	14 638 kHz (75 baud)
VOA, Tangier	5460, 13 770 kHz (75 baud)
XINHUA, China	14 367·5 kHz
ANSA, Rome	8052 kHz

Press pictures

Although most press photographs are now transmitted via
communications satellite channels or by landlines a few stations still
transmit these pictures on the HF bands using the photo facsimile
(photofax) system. The popular formats used are generally 60/288,
120/288, 120/576 or 240/576 with a frequency shift of 400 Hz each side
of the carrier frequency. The polarity of the video signal is usually
reversed to give a negative image. This can be corrected by receiving
the signal using the LSB mode. The direction of scanning for press
photos is from right to left.

Bands used for press photo transmissions are:

9800–10 800 kHz
13 500–14 000 kHz
15 600–16 100 kHz
18 500–19 000 kHz

Some sample frequencies are:

Norwegian press, Norway	9982 kHz 240/576
UPI, Belgium	10 727 kHz 120/288
AP, New York	10 340, 11 460, 15 825 kHz

Meteorological stations

One major group of utility stations are those which provide weather
and other meteorological information. These are normally
government operated stations.

Many of the meteorological stations transmit weather information
using RTTY at 50 baud. Unlike amateur and press teletype stations
these signals use a wide shift of 850 kHz. The transmissions are coded
and appear as strings of four or five figure groups giving data on a
variety of meteorological measurements. For more information on
the meaning of the codes used readers are referred to the *Meteo Code
Manual* published by Klingenfuss.

Most of these stations are in the bands:

3200–3350 kHz
3750–3850 kHz
4700–4990 kHz
5200–5500 kHz
7300–8200 kHz

Typical frequencies are:

Bracknell, UK	4489, 6835 kHz
Moscow, USSR	3330, 5120, 7685 kHz
New York, USA	8130 kHz
Miami, USA	8105 kHz
Halifax, Canada	9890 kHz

Weather charts

Many meteorological stations use facsimile transmissions to
broadcast weather charts of various kinds. Most use either 120/288 or
120/576 formats although Russian stations often use 60/288, 90/288

and 90/576 formats as well. The charts are simple black and white line drawings but some stations also transmit weather satellite photographs at certain times during the day. These facsimile signals can be found in the following bands:

4200–4800 kHz
5100–5500 kHz
7500–8000 kHz
10 000–10 500 kHz

Typical frequencies are:

Bracknell, UK	4610, 4782 kHz
Moscow, USSR	5150, 5355, 7670 kHz
Halifax, Canada	10 536, 13 510 kHz
Paris, France	4047, 8185 kHz
Hamburg, Germany	3885, 7880 kHz
Norfolk, Va, USA	8080, 10 865 kHz

Note for amateur meteorologists in the UK wishing to use the fax signals from Bracknell, permission should be obtained by writing to the Meteorological Office, Bracknell, Surrey. A special fax reception licence may be obtained by applying to the Radio Communications Division, Department of Trade and Industry, Waterloo Bridge House, London.

The aircraft bands

Several bands are set aside for use by aircraft and ground control stations. Most of the voice transmissions between aircraft and ground stations in these bands are for air traffic control. The HF bands are used for major transoceanic routes while VHF and UHF are used for communications along the airways routes over land or for approach and landing. The other type of station to be heard on the HF bands is the VOLMET (flying weather forecast) station which gives weather conditions for various airports.

HF air communications
The bands used for oceanic communications on HF are:

5480–5730 kHz
6525–6775 kHz
8800–9040 kHz
10 005–10 100 kHz
11 175–11 400 kHz
13 200–13 360 kHz
17 900–18 030 kHz
21 924–22 000 kHz

For the main intercontinental air routes the world is divided up into a number of air traffic control areas which cover North Atlantic, South Atlantic, Caribbean, Africa, Middle East, Indian Ocean, Far East, South America, North Pacific, South Pacific and Europe.
Some commonly used frequencies for the various major intercontinental routes are:

North Atlantic   3419, 5598, 5616, 5649, 8825, 8891, 11 279, 11 336 and 13 306 kHz

Caribbean	5520, 5550, 6577, 8846, 8918 and 11 387 kHz
Middle East	3467, 5667, 8918, 13 288 and 13 312 kHz
Africa	5493, 5652, 8861, 8895, 11 300, 11 360, 13 279 kHz
Indian Ocean	5634, 13 291, 13 306 and 17 961 kHz
Far East	5655, 5658, 6556, 6571, 8942, 13 309, 13 318 kHz

Some channels in the HF aircraft bands are used by individual airlines as a company frequency while others are allocated to major airports for long-range communications. Voice transmissions in the aircraft bands generally use SSB (upper sideband) and channels are normally spaced at 4 kHz intervals although adjacent channels are rarely used in the same control area. Some transmissions are made using CW or RTTY modes.

Commercial and military aircraft normally carry transponders which provide identification for ground radar stations. These are referred to as *squawk* signals. Selective calls (selcalls) consist of a combination of audio tones which are transmitted to the aircraft, decoded by its receiver and used to sound an alarm. Each aircraft has its own combination of tones so that one particular aircraft can be alerted when the controller wishes to communicate with it. This allows the pilot or engineer to concentrate on other tasks without having to continually monitor the radio channel.

VHF/UHF air communications
Most local air traffic controls, including approach, landing and communications while the aircraft is on the ground, are carried out using the VHF or UHF bands.

Civil aircraft and airports use frequencies in the band 118–136 MHz. Transmissions use AM (A3E) and channels are spaced at 50 kHz intervals. Simplex operation is used with the aircraft and tower on the same frequency.

Some typical frequencies are:

London, Heathrow	118·5, 118·7, 119·2, 119·5 MHz
London, Gatwick	119·6, 124·225, 127·55 MHz
Birmingham	118·3, 120·5 MHz
Manchester	118·7, 119·4, 124·2, 125·1 MHz
Prestwick	118·15, 120·55 MHz

Military airfields and aircraft generally use the band from 225–400 MHz although some frequencies in the 118–138 MHz band are also used. Transmissions are simplex using AM (A3E).

VOLMET transmissions
VOLMET stations provide weather and meteorological broadcast services for aircraft. They generally operate all day but switch frequency from time to time as propagation changes. Some VOLMET stations in the Europe and North American area are:

Europe	Shannon	3413, 5640 kHz
	RAF	4722, 11 200 kHz
North America	New York, USA	3485, 10 051, 13 270 kHz
	Gander, Canada	3485, 10 051, 13 270 kHz

VHF VOLMET stations in the UK operate on 126·6 and 128·6 MHz.

Air band terminology and abbreviations
Some common terms used on the aircraft bands are:

ADF	Automatic direction finder
AFIS	Airfield flight information service
Altitude	Height (quoted in 100 feet units)
ATC	Air traffic control

ATIS	Automatic terminal information service
CAV ok	Ceiling and visibility OK
CAT	Clear air turbulence
DME	Distance measuring equipment
ETA	Estimated time of arrival
FIR	Flight information region
Gear	Undercarriage
Glidepath	Approach path for landing using ILS
Greens	Undercarriage down indicators
IFR	Instrument flight rules
ILS	Instrument landing system
IMC	Instrument meteorological conditions
Knots	Nautical miles per hour (used for air speed)
Localizer	Beacon on glide path
Mach	Airspeed in terms of the speed of sound
MATZ	Military airfield traffic zone
No sig	No significant weather conditions
NOTAM	Notice to airmen
Okta	One eighth (used for cloud density)
Orbit	Fly a circular holding path
PAR	Precision Approach Radar
Pax	Passengers
QDM	Magnetic heading
QFE	Barometric pressure at an airport
QNH	Barometric pressure at sea level
RVR	Runway visual range
SARBE	Search and rescue beacon
Selcal	Selective call system
Sit Rep	Situation report
SRA	Surveillance radar approach
Squawk	Switch on identification transponder
Stratus	Low misty cloud
TACAN	Tactical navigation system
TAR	Terminal area radar
UIR	Upper flight information region
VFR	Visual flight rules
VMC	Visual meteorological conditions
VOLMET	Flying weather forecast
VOR	VHF omni range beacon
VORTAC	Combined VOR/DME system (VOR/TACAN)
VSI	Vertical speed (rate of climb) indicator
Wilco	Will comply

Maritime radio

A large part of the HF radio spectrum is allocated for use by ships
and other maritime services. There are many coastal stations which
provide communication with ships. The VHF band is used for short-
range communications such as control of traffic in port areas and for
private boats operating near the coast.

The HF maritime bands are:

4000–4438 kHz	12 230–13 200 kHz
6200–6525 kHz	16 360–17 410 kHz
8100–8812 kHz	22 000–22 855 kHz

For CW (Morse) operation the channel spacing depends upon the frequency band used. Different groups of channels are used for calling and working frequencies.

CW calling channels are:

4180·0–4187·2 kHz	(18 channels 400 Hz apart)
6270·0–6280·8 kHz	(18 channels 600 Hz apart)
8360·0–8374·4 kHz	(18 channels 800 Hz apart)
12 540·6–12 561·0 kHz	(18 channels 1·2 kHz apart)
16 720·0–16 748·8 kHz	(18 channels 1·6 kHz apart)
22 228·0–22 246·0 kHz	(10 channels 2·0 kHz apart)

CW working channels are:

4188·5–4219·0 kHz	(62 channels × 500 Hz)
6282·75–6325·0 kHz	(44 channels × 750 Hz)
8377·0–8435·0 kHz	(116 channels × 500 Hz)
12 565·5–12 652·0 kHz	(174 channels × 500 Hz)
16 754·0–16 858·5 kHz	(208 channels × 500 Hz)
22 250·5–22 310·0 kHz	(120 channels × 500 Hz)

Many of the maritime channels are designed to operate in the duplex mode where the ship station transmits on one frequency and the coastal station on a second frequency.

For telephony operation upper single sideband is used. Channels are spaced 3·1 kHz apart and the main groups of duplex channels are:

4063·0–4140·5 kHz	Channels 401–426	Ship
4357·4–4434·9 kHz	Channels 401–426	Shore
6200·0–6215·5 kHz	Channels 601–606	Ship
6506·4–6521·9 kHz	Channels 601–606	Shore
8195·0–8288·0 kHz	Channels 801–831	Ship
8718·9–8811·9 kHz	Channels 801–831	Shore
12 330·0–12 426·1 kHz	Channels 1201–1232	Ship
13 100·0–13 196·9 kHz	Channels 1201–1232	Shore
16 460·0–16 584·0 kHz	Channels 1601–1641	Ship
17 232·9–17 356·9 kHz	Channels 1601–1641	Shore
22 000·0–22 120·9 kHz	Channels 2201–2240	Ship
22 596·0–22 716·9 kHz	Channels 2201–2240	Shore

Some maritime transmissions use radioteletype (RTTY) at 50 baud and a number of duplex channels are set aside for this mode of operation. The SITOR system may also be used on these channels. Channels are spaced at 500 kHz intervals and frequencies are as follows:

4170·5–4177·0 MHz	14 ship channels
4350·0–4356·5 MHz	14 shore channels
6256·5–6267·5 MHz	23 ship channels
6494·5–6505·5 MHz	23 shore channels
8344·0–8357·0 MHz	27 ship channels
8705·0–8718·0 MHz	27 shore channels
12 491·5–12 519·5 MHz	57 ship channels
13 071·5–13 099·5 MHz	57 shore channels
16 660·5–16 705·5 MHz	69 ship channels
17 197·5–17 231·5 MHz	69 shore channels
22 192·5–22 225·5 MHz	67 ship channels
22 561·5–22 594·5 MHz	67 shore channels

Most of the other frequencies in the shipping bands are used by coastal stations and for special facilities such as selective calling.

Maritime terms and abbreviations

AA	All after ... (repetition request)
AB	All before ... (repetition request)
ADS	Address
ANUL	Delete
BN	All between ... and ... (repetition request)
CES	Coast earth station (for INMARSAT)
Draught	Height between waterline and ship's bottom
ETA	Estimated time of arrival
ETD	Estimated time of departure
Fairway	Navigable part of seaway
FMT	Format error
INMARSAT	Geostationary satellite link for ship/shore or ship/ship communication
KA	Start of message
KN	End of message
LX	Delux greetings radiotelegram
Mark	Navigation mark or buoy
MAYDAY	Distress call (radiotelephony)
MOM	Please wait/I am waiting
MRCC	Marine rescue coordination centre
MUT	Message was mutilated
NX	Notice to mariners
OBS	Meteorological service radiotelegram
OCC	The subscriber is engaged
OL	Radiomaritime ocean letter
PAN	Emergency call for medical help
PBL	Preamble (repetition request)
PRESSE	Press radiotelegram
RAP	I shall call you back
RPx	Reply paid radiotelegram
RTL	Radio telex letter
SECURITE	Safety call (navigation or meteorological warning by telephony)
SIG	Signature
SLT	Ship letter telegram
SOS	Distress call (radiotelegraphy)
SVP	Please
TELEX	An international teletype service
TPR	Teleprinter
TR	Traffic routing message
TTT	Safety call (navigation or meteorological warning by telegraphy)
TXT	Text
USCG	US coast guard
WA	Word after ... (repetition request)
WB	Word before ... (repetition request)
WRU	Who are you?
WX	Weather report
YZ	Words which follow are in plain language

Other utility stations

The HF bands contain many other utility stations including telecommunications links, such as telephone or telex services, and military communications. These are often difficult to identify or use transmission modes which are not readily decoded. Several books are available which provide lists of these confidential frequencies and give some indication of times at which signals may be heard.

The VHF and UHF bands are used for public service communications systems, such as police, fire, or ambulance services and private mobile radio systems such as those used by taxis. Most of these transmissions have the base station and the mobile transmitter on different frequencies. In some cases repeaters are used to provide wider coverage. Other stations in these bands include the cellular radio links for mobile car telephones and some paging services. Two small bands are used for radio controlled models.

General frequency allocations in the UK are:

Private mobile radio (PMR)

85·0125–86·2875 ⎱	Base Tx	Two frequency simplex
71·3125–72·7875 ⎰	Mobile Tx	12·5 kHz channels
86·9625–87·5000 ⎱	Base Tx	Two frequency simplex
76·9625–77·5000 ⎰	Mobile Tx	12·5 kHz channels
86·3000–86·7000	Simplex	12·5 kHz channels
165·050–168·250 ⎱	Base Tx	Two frequency simple
169·850–173·050 ⎰	Mobile Tx	12·5 kHz channels
168·950–169·850	Simplex	12·5 kHz channels
176·500–183·500 ⎱	Base Tx	Split simplex
184·500–191·500 ⎰	Mobile Tx	12·5 kHz channels
200·500–207·500 ⎱	Base Tx	Split simplex
192·500–199·500 ⎰	Mobile Tx	12·5 kHz channels
208·500–215·500 ⎱	Base Tx	Split simplex
216·500–223·500 ⎰	Mobile Tx	12·5 kHz channels
453·025–453·975 ⎱	Base Tx	Split simplex
459·325–460·475 ⎰	Mobile Tx	12·5 kHz channels
456·000–456·975 ⎱	Base Tx	Split simplex
461·500–462·475 ⎰	Mobile Tx	12·5 kHz channels
488·006–448·994 ⎱	Base Tx	(London area only)
431·006–431·994 ⎰	Mobile Tx	(London area only)
163·0375–164·4250 ⎱	Base Tx	Radiophone
158·5350–159·9125 ⎰	Mobile Tx	Split simplex
935·0125–949·9875 ⎱	Base Tx	Cellular radio
890·0125–904·9875 ⎰	Mobile Tx	Duplex

Radio paging transmitters

26·9570–27·2830	On-site paging
31·7250–31·7750	On-site paging
153·025–153·475	Wide area paging
161·000–161·100	Acknowledgement channels
454·0125–454·8250	Wide area paging
459·100–459·500	On site paging

Model control bands
35·005–35·205 MHz
458·50–459·50 MHz

6
Space communications

This section covers the transmission and reception of signals from space vehicles, via communications satellites and via reflection from other bodies in space such as the moon.

Space satellites can generally be grouped into three major types according to the type of orbit they follow as they travel over the surface of the earth. The three orbit types are low altitude near circular orbits, high altitude elliptical orbits and synchronous or geostationary orbits. For tracking calculations the low orbit satellites are usually assumed to have circular, or near circular, orbits around the earth (Figure 18).

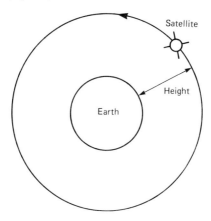

Figure 18   Basic near circular satellite orbit

Satellite parameters

For circular and elliptical orbit satellites the position of the satellite relative to the ground station changes with time and communication is only possible when the satellite is in view of the ground station. For low altitude satellites the orbit is usually assumed to be circular to simplify tracking calculations.

The main parameters for a low altitude near circular orbit satellite are:

Apogee   The point in its orbit where the satellite is furthest from the earth.
Perigee   The point in the orbit where the satellite is closest to earth.
Ascending node (EQX)   The point in the orbit where the satellite crosses the earth's equatorial plane travelling south to north.

Descending node   The point of equatorial crossing when travelling north to south.

EQX time   The time at which EQX occurs given in universal time (etc.).

EQX longitude   The position around the equator at which EQX occurs. Measured as degrees west.

Period   The time taken for one complete orbit (i.e. between successive EQX times).

Inclination   The angle between the orbital plane of the satellite and the equatorial plane of the earth.

Acquisition of signal (AOS)   The time at which the satellite comes above the horizon and in sight of the ground station.

Loss of signal (LOS)   The time at which the satellite drops below the horizon out of sight of the ground station.

Azimuth   The direction of the satellite in the horizontal plane relative to the ground station. Measured as an angle clockwise from north.

Elevation   The angle of the satellite above the horizontal relative to the ground station.

Russian satellites have inclination angles less than 90° and the satellite orbit climbs to the east of the north pole on the ascending part of the orbit. American satellites have inclination angles greater than 90° and their orbits climb to the west of the North Pole.

Calculations for predicting the AOS and LOS times, azimuth and elevation angles are relatively complex and require the use of an electronic calculator or personal computer. Satellite tracking programs for use on popular home computers are available from a number of sources. The basic information needed for tracking near earth satellites is EQX, inclination and period.

An alternative tracking technique uses a polar projection map of the world together with a ground track overlay. One scheme is the *oscarlocator* which requires the EQX time and longitude.

Low orbit satellites give relatively short communications periods when the satellite is visible from the ground station.

For satellites which are in an elliptical orbit the apogee is very much greater than perigee. When the satellite is near apogee the period of visibility to the ground station is much greater than for a low orbit satellite. A set of Keplerian elements is used to calculate the satellite track. Additional parameters used for tracking these satellites are:

Eccentricity   A value which indicates the flatness of the ellipse relative to a circle which has an eccentricity of zero.

Right ascension of the ascending node (RAAN)   This defines the satellite position in relation to a set of coordinates based on a fixed point in space. This reference is the first point of Aries and the RAAN is the angle between the line of nodes and a line to the point in Aries.

Argument of perigee   The angle between a line from the earth centre to perigee and a second line from the earth centre to the point where the orbit crosses the equator at the EQX time.

Mean anomaly   The angular position (phase) of the satellite around its orbit measured from perigee.

Mean motion   The number of passes through the perigee point per day.

Epoch   The time at which the parameters were measured. Usually given as year, day and decimal fraction of day.

Once again a computer program can be used to calculate times at which the satellite is visible. A map and overlay system may also be used to track this type of satellite and an example is the *Phase 3 tracker*.

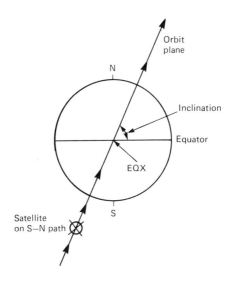

Figure 19   *Diagram showing orbit inclination and EQX for a satellite orbit*

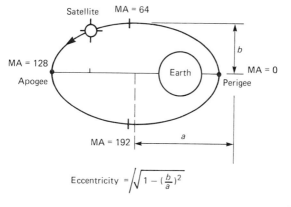

Figure 20   *Basic elliptical type satellite orbit*

Orbital parameter newscasts

Some news broadcasts and networks on the amateur bands provide information on the orbit parameters of amateur satellites (AMSAT) as follows:

ARRL News　　　EQX times and longitudes
Monday–Friday
CW　　at 0100, 0400, 1500, 2200 GMT
　　　　on 3580, 7080, 14 070, 21 080, 28 080 kHz
SSB　　at 0230, 0530 GMT
　　　　on 3990, 7290, 14 290, 21 390, 28 590 kHz
RTTY　at 0200, 0500, 1600, 2300 GMT
　　　　on 3625, 7095, 14 095, 21 095, 28 095 kHz

AMSAT (USA) Network　　Parameters and other satellite news
Wednesday　0200 GMT　3855 kHz SSB
Sunday　　　1800 GMT　21 280 kHz SSB
Sunday　　　1900 GMT　14 282 kHz SSB

AMSAT (Europe) Network　　Parameters and satellite news
Saturday　1000 GMT　14 280 kHz SSB

AMSAT (UK) Network　　Satellite news
Sunday　1015 local time　3780 kHz SSB

Other sources of satellite parameters are the magazines of AMSAT in the USA and UK, Practical Wireless and Short Wave Magazine.

Geostationary satellites

If the satellite is placed in an equatorial orbit at a height of 22 247 miles the satellite travels around its orbit in twenty-four hours. If the satellite motion is in the same direction as the rotation of the earth the satellite remains at a fixed position above the equator. This type of orbit is known as synchronous or geostationary. The geostationary orbit is divided into a series of slots which are referred to by the longitude point over which the satellite is placed. The elevation and azimuth angles for the ground receiving antenna can be calculated from the satellite longitude position and the latitude and longitude of the ground station. Only those satellites which appear above the horizon when viewed from the ground station can be received. Reception will also depend upon the direction in which the satellite antenna is beamed. The area on the earth's surface covered by the beam of the satellite antenna is generally known as its *footprint*.

Geostationary satellites are used for the main intercontinental communications links and for television signal distribution and broadcasting.

Amateur satellites

A number of amateur radio satellites for communications and for scientific experiments have been placed into orbit in space. The

following segments of the amateur bands are allocated for use with
space satellites:

7·000–7·100 MHz	5650·0–5670·0 MHz
14·000–14·250 MHz	5830·0–5850·0 MHz
21·000–21·450 MHz	10·450–10·500 GHz
28·000–29·700 MHz	24·000–24·050 GHz
144·00–146·00 MHz	47·000–47·200 GHz
435·00–438·00 MHz	75·500–76·000 GHz
1260·0–1270·0 MHz	142·00–144·00 GHz
2400·0–2450·0 MHz	248·00–250·00 GHz

Communications transponders

On satellites used for communications a wide band transponder is
used which accepts all signals within the uplink passband and
retransmits them at corresponding frequencies within the down link
passband. Transponders may be either non-inverting or inverting
types (Figure 21). An inverting transponder generally gives less
trouble with Doppler shift since the uplink and down link shifts tend
to cancel.

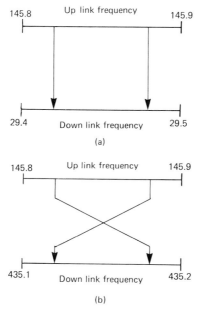

Figure 21 *Relationship between uplink and downlink frequencies for a
satellite transponder:*
(a) Non-inverting type
(b) Inverting type

On a non-inverting transponder the down link frequency is given by:

$$f_d = f_u - f_t$$

Where f_t is the translation frequency. Signals in the down link band have the same frequency order as those in the up link band.

On an inverting transponder the down link frequency is given by:

$$f_d = f_t - f_u$$

and signals in the down link band are transposed relative to those in the uplink band.

Due to the motion of the satellite relative to the ground station there is a frequency shift of the received signal due to the Doppler effect. This shift is proportional to the frequency of the signal and for low orbit satellites the typical worst case values for the amateur bands are:

Band	Doppler shift
29 MHz	700 Hz
144 MHz	3 kHz
432 MHz	10 kHz
1260 MHz	29 kHz

The maximum shift depends upon orbit height with the shift reducing as the height increases. For a non-inverting transponder the shifts for the uplink and downlink must be added together. For an inverting transponder the difference between the shifts for the uplink and downlink will apply. For an elliptical orbit satellite (e.g. OSCAR 10) the Doppler shift at apogee is typically about an eighth of that for perigee or for a low orbit satellite.

Operating modes

Mode A	Uplink	145·850–145·950
	Downlink	29·400–29·500
Mode B	Uplink	435 MHz
	Downlink	145 MHz
Mode C	Low power mode B	
Mode D	Telemetry only	
Mode J	Uplink	145·800–146·000
	Downlink	435·000–438·000
Mode JA	Uplink	145·900–146·000
	Downlink	435·800–435·900
Mode JD	Uplink	145·850–145·910
	Downlink	435·910
	Digital transponder for packet radio	
	Four channels spaced at 20 kHz on 145 MHz	
	Single channel downlink on 435 MHz	
Mode K	Uplink	21 MHz
	Downlink	29 MHz
Mode L	Uplink	1260·00–1270·00
	Downlink	435·00–438·00
Mode T	Uplink	21 MHz
	Downlink	145 MHz

Satellite band plans

On OSCAR satellites the down link band is divided up into five
segments. At each end of the band are the beacons and a 25 kHz wide
band for special services such as news broadcasts. The central
124 kHz wide band is divided into three segments for CW only, mixed
CW/SSB and SSB only (Figure 22). Russian satellites, which
generally have a narrower transponder bandwidth, use a similar
bandplan with CW signals at the lower frequency end. It should be
noted that on a reverse transponder the CW signals are transmitted
in the upper part of the uplink passband.

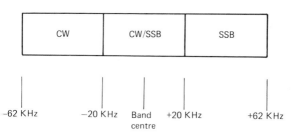

Figure 22   *General band plan for OSCAR satellites.*

Satellite telemetry

Satellites normally carry a number of beacon transmitters which
allow the satellite to be detected as it comes into range of the ground
stations. In some cases the beacons in use will also indicate which
transponders are operational.

All amateur satellites transmit telemetry signals which give the
status of various parameters within the satellite. These signals are
normally sent using Morse code on the satellite beacon frequencies.
The telemetry consists of a string of numbers giving data for the
various channels in sequence. The University of Surrey Satellite
(UOSAT) OSCAR 9 satellite also carries a voice synthesizer which
may be used for telemetry.

OSCAR phase 2 satellites
These satellites carry communications transponders and telemetry
transmitters. They are placed into a near circular low orbit and
provide relatively short periods of communications as they pass over
a ground station. Examples were OSCAR 7 and OSCAR 8 which
have now ceased operation.

OSCAR phase 3 satellites
These satellites are launched into an elliptical orbit which permits
relatively long periods of communications when the apogee of the
satellite is on the same side of the earth as the ground station.

Communications transponders, beacons and telemetry are provided on these satellites. An example of this type of satellite is OSCAR 10:

Mode B	Up	435·025–435·175 MHz
	Down	145·975–145·825 MHz
Beacons		145·812, 145·900 MHz
Mode L	Up	1269·05–1269·85 MHz
	Down	436·950–436·150 MHz
Beacons		436·040, 436·020 MHz

Note both transponders are inverting.

UOSAT satellites

UOSAT satellites were produced by the University of Surrey and the UK AMSAT organization for scientific research experiments. UOSAT1 (OSCAR UO9) carries telemetry and beacon transmitters and an imager camera to give pictures of the earth's surface. This satellite is not intended for communications purposes. UOSAT 2 (OSCAR UO11) is similar to UOSAT 1 but carries different experiments.

UOSAT1 (UO9)   HF beacons 7050, 14 002, 21 002, 29510 kHz CW
VHF beacon/telemetry 145·825 MHz FM
UHF beacon/telemetry 435·025 MHz FM
S band beacon/telemetry 2401·0 MHz FM
Microwave beacon 10 470 MHz CW

Imager system 256 × 256 pixels digital coded with 4 bits per pixel.
Uses VHF/UHF beacon Tx.
Period 95·3 minutes. Inclination 97·48°.

UOSAT2 (UO11)   VHF beacon/telemetry 145·825 MHz FM
UHF beacon/telemetry 435·025 MHz FM
S band beacon/telemetry 2401·5 MHz FM

Period 98·56 Minutes. Inclination 98·25°.

Fuji satellite (OSCAR 12)

The first Japanese satellite, Fuji 1 (OSCAR FO12), is designed to act as a communications satellite using mode JA and carries a mode JD packet radio repeater with a store and forward message handling facility.

Mode JA	Up	145·900–145·933 MHz SSB
		145·933–145·967 MHz CW/SSB
		145·967–146·000 MHz CW
	Down	435·900–435·867 MHz SSB
		435·867–435·833 MHz CW/SSB
		435·833–435·800 MHz CW
Mode JD	Up	145·85 (Ch1), 145·87 (Ch2),
		145·89 (Ch3), 145·91 (Ch4)
	Down	435·910 MHz

Mode JA   Transponder is inverting type.
Period 115·8 minutes. Inclination 50°. Height 1498 km.

Russian satellites

Russian amateur satellites are given code names RS followed by a serial number. Satellites RS1 to RS11 have been launched but, of these, only RS5, RS7, RS10 and RS11 are now active. Early satellites used Mode A transponders but the latest satellites RS10 and RS11 use modes A, K and T.

Each of these four satellites carries a robot system which provides automatic Morse contacts. The RS11 robot transmits on one of its 29 MHz beacon frequencies using the format 'CQ de RS11 QSU 21 300 AR' and listens on 21 300 kHz for calls which should have the format 'RS11 de (your call) AR'. The robot responds by sending the call sign received and a QSO number. The robot on the other RS satellites operates in a similar fashion. Telemetry signals are sent using Morse code.

RS10 and RS11 may also use two additional transponder modes. In mode KA the 21 and 145 MHz uplink signals are combined to give a single down link on 29 MHz. For mode KT the up link is on 21 MHz and the down link is transmitted on both 29 MHz and 145 MHz at the same time.

RS5

Transponder	Up link	145·910–145·950 MHz
	Down link	29·410–29·450 MHz
Robot	Up link	145·826 MHz
	Down link	29·331 or 29·452 MHz
Beacons and telemetry		29·331 or 29·452 MHz

Transponder is non-inverting
Period 119·5 minutes. Inclination 82·95°. Height 1690 km.

RS7

Transponder	Up link	145·960–146·000 MHz
	Down link	29·460–29·500 MHz
Robot (CW)	Up link	145·835 MHz
	Down link	29·341 or 29·501 MHz
Beacon/telemetry (CW)		29·341 or 29·501 MHz

Transponder is non-inverting
Period 119·14 minutes. Inclination 82·95°. Height 1698 km.

RS10

Transponders (non-inverting type)

Mode A	Up link	145·860–145·900 MHz
	Down link	29·360–29·400 MHz
Mode K	Up link	21·160–21·200 MHz
	Down link	29·360–29·400 MHz
Mode T	Up link	21·160–21·200 MHz
	Down link	145·860–145·900 MHz
Robot	Up link	21·120 or 145·820 MHz
	Down link	29·357 or 29·403 MHz
Beacon/telemetry		29·357, 29·403 MHz
		145·857, 145·903 MHz

RS11

Transponders (non-inverting type)

Mode A	Up link	145·910–145·950 Mhz
	Down link	29·410–29·450 MHz
Mode K	Up link	21·210–21·250 MHz
	Down link	29·410–29·450 MHz

Mode T	Up link	21·210–21·450 MHz
	Down link	145·910–145·950 MHz
Robot	Up link	21·130 or 145·830 MHz
	Down link	29·407 or 29·453 MHz
Beacon/telemetry		29·407, 29·453 MHz
		145·907, 145·953 MHz

RS10 and RS11 share the same space vehicle with an orbital period of 105·2 minutes and inclination of 82·93° and an increment of 26·26° on each orbit.

Weather satellites

One form of satellite signal reception which can be of interest is the reception of facsimile pictures from the various weather satellites that are in orbit. Many of these transmissions are made in the 137 MHz band and are easily received with a modified VHF converter. An international system known as *wefax* (weather facsimile) also provides satellite picture signals and operates at a frequency of 1691 MHz. Images from the spacecraft are initially transmitted to ground using a special high resolution mode and then converted at the ground station to the standard APT mode and sent back to the satellite from which the picture is rebroadcast for reception by simpler ground stations.

Weather satellites fall into two major groups. The first are the low altitude satellites which tend to have near polar orbits and transmit downlink signals in the 137 MHz band. The American satellites of this type are called the National Oceanic and Atmospheric Administration (NOAA) series while the Russian satellites of this type are the METEOR series. There are some differences in the format of the facsimile signals from the US and Russian satellites they both use 120 lines per minute and the video signal uses amplitude modulation of an audio frequency subcarrier which is then used to frequency modulate the 137 MHz carrier signal.

The NOAA satellites normally transmit a pair of pictures side by side with one giving the visual image and the second an infrared image. Russian satellites usually transmit one picture image and this is generally a visual image.

The received facsimile picture can be reproduced by using a conventional facsimile machine but for amateur stations it is more common to use some form of computer display system. This might use one of the popular home computers to provide a high resolution graphics picture with perhaps eight grey levels and a resolution of, say, 256 pixels. More advanced home computers may permit higher resolution or perhaps sixteen grey levels to give improved pictures. A permanent copy of the received picture may then be obtained by dumping the graphics display to a dot matrix type printer.

It is also possible to actually store the picture using even higher resolution of perhaps 1024 by 1024 pixels and then display part of the picture at a time with high resolution or the whole picture with reduced resolution. The main constraint here is the amount of computer memory that is available for storing the picture information. An alternative approach is to use a dedicated display system which basically consists of a large digital memory to act as a frame store and a digital graphics display which will generally use some form of television monitor.

Apart from the picture transmissions the weather satellites may also transmit weather data using RTTY signals where the data is in the form of groups of numbers following a similar format to that used by ground based weather transmissions.

Frequencies used by these low level satellites are as follows:

NOAA6	137·500 MHz
NOAA9	137·620 MHz
METEOR1	137·850 MHz
METEOR2–9	137·300 MHz
METEOR2–13	137·400 MHz
METEOR3–1	137·850 MHz
COSMOS	137·400 MHz

Orbit predictions and transmission schedule for the NOAA satellites is broadcast by RTTY from Bracknell on 4489 kHz daily between 1930 and 2030 GMT.

The second type of weather satellite operates in a geostationary orbit over the equator. The satellites transmit facsimile pictures for the WEFAX service. The speed used is 240 lines per minute using the APT transmission format. Six of these satellites are eventually planned to be in orbit to give worldwide coverage and have the following orbit positions:

METEOSAT	0°	Europe
GOES East	75° W	USA
GOES Central	105° W	USA
GOES West	130° W	USA
GOMS	70° E	USSR
GMS	140° E	JAPAN

The transmission frequency is normally 1691·000 MHz but the METEOSAT frequency is 1694·500 MHz.

Spacecraft communications

Another type of signal that may be received from space is the communications downlink between a spacecraft such as the US Space Shuttle or the Russian Soyuz craft or space stations and their ground control stations. Russian spacecraft use frequencies around 20 MHz and 142 MHz. American shuttle transmissions may sometimes be found in the 250–300 MHz band.

Satellite television

Television signals are transmitted via satellites operating in the 3·5–4·5 GHz (C band) and 10–12 GHz (K band) microwave channels. The C band communications satellites are used for intercontinental links between broadcasting networks and for feeds to cable networks. Some communications satellites also operate in the 10·5–11·5 GHz

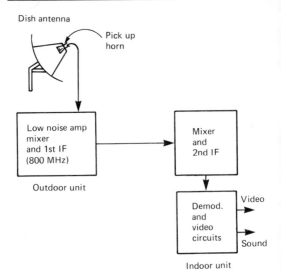

Figure 23   *Basic system for reception of satellite TV signals*

band. Satellites operating in the 11·5–12·5 GHz band are used for direct broadcasting by satellite (DBS) television services. The 4 and 11 GHz communications satellites use relatively low power transmitters and require the use of dish aerials with a diameter of 1·5 m or more at the ground station to provide satisfactory TV reception. DBS satellites have higher powered transmitters giving signal levels in the main service area which permit good reception using a receiving dish antenna of less than 1 m diameter.

Each communications satellite carries up to twenty-four separate transponders, each having a bandwidth of some 36 MHz. In many cases a transponder is occupied by a single television channel but on some satellites two television signals may be carried using one transponder. Transponders which are not being used for television carry other services such as intercontinental telephone channels, and various other radio channels.

On C band satellites the uplink frequencies are in the range 5945–6405 MHz and downlink frequencies run from 3720–4380 MHz. The centre frequencies of the twenty-four channels in this band are spaced 20 MHz apart. Because each channel is 36 MHz wide the adjacent channels overlap in frequency so their signals are polarized in different directions (e.g. vertically and horizontally) to reduce interference. Channels with the same polarization are spaced 40 MHz apart.

On K band satellites the uplink is in the range 14·00–14·50 GHz and the downlink is in the range 10·95–11·20 GHz and 11·45–11·70 GHz. For direct broadcast satellites the downlink is in the range 11·70–12·50 GHz.

The European DBS band is divided into forty channels each 36 MHz wide and spaced at 19 MHz intervals. Adjacent channels overlap in frequency but interference is avoided by arranging that adjacent transponders use a different antenna polarization.

At present amateur space satellites do not cater for television transmissions but it is possible that future satellite projects may include a transponder for fast scan television signals.

For satellite transmission the television signal is frequency modulated on to its carrier and several sound subcarriers may be included to provide different language sound channels. Sound subcarrier frequencies on the channels vary from 5 MHz to 8 MHz and are generally FM. Most video signals currently use one of the normal broadcast standards with colour by NTSC, PAL or SECAM methods. In future some European channels will use a version of the MAC standard.

Communications type satellites are used to provide TV services for cable networks or paying subscribers and some form of scrambling may be used to prevent unauthorized viewing. On the video signal this usually takes the form of altering the sync pulse so that a conventional TV set cannot lock the picture correctly while for sound some form of analogue scrambling technique may be used. Some channels broadcast the sound as a digital signal within the sync pulse period and this digital signal may be enciphered before transmission so that only receivers with an appropriate decoder unit can decipher the sound. Direct broadcast channels are not usually scrambled.

The receiving station for satellite television consists of a dish antenna which focuses the signal on to a feed horn mounted at the focus of the dish. Signals from the feed horn are fed to a low noise amplifier and converter which produces an IF in the region of 800–1000 MHz. This signal is fed via cable to an indoor receiver which contains the channel tuning and an IF amplifier with a bandwidth of the order 25 MHz and an FM demodulator to produce the video output and sound subcarriers. In most systems the video and sound are remodulated on to a UHF carrier such as channel 36 and then fed to the aerial input of a standard television receiver.

In the multiplexed analogue components (MAC) system the luminance and chrominance signals are transmitted separately by using a time multiplexing system (Figure 24). The luminance signal is compressed to fit into two-thirds of the line scan period and the chrominance signal is sent during the remaining one-third of the line period. Synchronization and sound make use of digital signals in the line blanking period at the start of each line scan. The compression and expansion of the analogue components of the video signal are

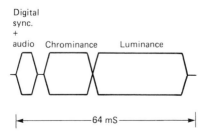

Figure 24   *The format of a single scan line of a MAC encoded television signal*

achieved by using digital techniques and special integrated circuits are available to provide the signal processing required in the receiver.

For multiplexed analogue component type transmissions and scrambled signals a decoder unit is included after the main intermediate frequency detector to extract the video and sound signals and convert them to a form suitable for a normal TV receiver.

European DBS channels

Channel number	Frequency GHz	Channel number	Frequency GHz
01	11·727	21	12·111
02	11·746	22	12·130
03	11·765	23	12·149
04	11·785	24	12·168
05	11·804	25	12·187
06	11·823	26	12·206
07	11·842	27	12·226
08	11·861	28	12·245
09	11·880	29	12·264
10	11·900	30	12·283
11	11·919	31	12·302
12	11·938	32	12·322
13	11·957	33	12·341
14	11·976	34	12·360
15	11·995	35	12·379
16	12·015	36	12·398
17	12·034	37	12·417
18	12·053	38	12·437
19	12·072	39	12·456
20	12·091	40	12·475

European channel allocations

Country	Orbit slot	Channels
Belgium	19 W	21, 25, 29, 33, 37
Britain	31 W	4, 8, 12, 16, 20
Denmark	5 E	12, 15, 20, 27, 35
Finland	5 E	2, 6, 10, 22, 26
France	19 W	1, 5, 9, 13, 17
Germany (West)	19 W	2, 6, 10, 14, 18
Ireland	31 W	2, 6, 10, 14, 18
Luxembourg	19 W	3, 7, 11, 15, 19
Netherlands	19 W	23, 27, 31, 35, 39
Norway	5 E	14, 18, 28, 32, 38
Portugal	31 W	3, 7, 11, 15, 19
Spain	31 W	23, 27, 31, 35, 39
Sweden	5 E	4, 8, 30, 34, 40

Russian Gorizont TV satellite
Moscow program 1   3675 GHz
Moscow program 2   3825 GHz

The satellite is located at orbit slot 14° W.

Other satellite TV channels

Programme	Orbit slot	Frequency GHz
Arts Channel	27·5 W	11·135
Children's Channel	27·5 W	11·015
Cable news	27·5 W	11·155
Filmnet	13·0 E	11·140
Premiere	27·5 W	11·015
RAI Italy	13·0 E	11·005
RTL Plus Luxembourg	13·0 E	11·091
SAT1 Germany	13·0 E	11·507
Screen Sport	27·5 W	11·135
SKY Channel	13·0 E	11·650
Super Channel	13·0 E	11·674
TV5 France	13·0 E	11·471
Teleclub	13·0 E	10·986
Worldnet	13·0 E	11·471
3-SAT Germany	13·0 E	11·055

Moonbounce contacts

Some amateur stations use the surface of the moon as a passive
satellite reflector to make long distance contacts on UHF and SHF
bands. This requires highly directional dish type antennas and very
low noise receivers. Frequencies used for earth-moon-earth (EME)
operation are:

144·000–144·025 MHz
432·000–432·025 MHz
1296·000–1296·025 MHz

7
Radio propagation

If the antenna of a transmitter were located in free space and radiated equally in all directions the signal strength at some distance r from the transmitter would be given by:

$$E = \frac{\sqrt{(30.P)}}{r} \text{ V/m}$$

Where P is the transmitter power in watts and r is the distance in metres between transmitting and receiving antennas.

· Here it will be seen that the signal strength falls off in inverse proportion to the distance. This ideal situation would apply in the case of communications between two space vehicles. For most applications the transmitting and receiving antennas are located near the ground and the transmitted signal consists of a 'ground wave' travelling over the ground surface and a 'sky wave' which is radiated into the atmosphere.

Ground wave propagation

Over a perfect conducting surface the ground wave falls off inversely with distance. In practice the ground is not a good conductor and causes further attenuation of the signal. At frequencies up to 200 kHz the attenuation is relatively low and propagation over thousands of kilometres is possible. At higher frequencies the ground wave attenuation increases rapidly with frequency and propagation range falls.

Ground wave propagation is used during daylight for MF band broadcasting giving good signals. Ground wave radiation from a horizontal antenna is small so MF broadcast stations generally use a vertical antenna. On the HF bands ground wave propagation is limited to a few miles and is useful only for local contacts.

The ionosphere

For HF propagation the sky wave is used because it can be reflected by the ionized layers in the upper regions of the earth's atmosphere. The effect of these ionized layers is to bend the path of the wave and to allow it to be reflected back to earth thus giving communications paths which are much longer than those provided by the ground wave. There are three major ionized layers in the atmosphere which are referred to as the D, E and F layers (Figure 25).

The D layer
The D layer is the lowest and exists at a height of 70–90 km. This layer exists only during daylight and is most intensely ionized at midday. The D layer does not reflect MF and HF signals but produces absorption as the wave passes through the layer. This layer restricts long-range propagation on 1·8 and 3·5 MHz during daylight.

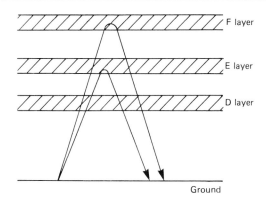

Figure 25   *The ionized layers in the ionosphere*

The E layer

Above the D layer at a height of 100–120 km is the E layer. This layer reflects signals in the MF and lower HF bands to provide propagation up to perhaps 1500 km during daylight. After dark the intensity of the E layer falls off but it does not completely disappear. At night this layer can provide long distance MF propagation.

The F layer

The upper ionized layer is known as the F layer. During daylight it splits into two layers: F_1 at about 150 km and F_2 at 300 km. After dark the F_1 and F_2 layers merge and the ionization level falls slowly. The F layer provides the main long-distance propagation path for the HF bands with lower frequency bands becoming more effective at night. The effectiveness of the F layer follows a cyclic change through the year giving best results on bands above 10 MHz during summer and below 10 MHz during winter. This layer is also affected by the activity of the sun and follows an eleven year cycle which is related to the number of sunspots on the sun's surface. At sunspot maximum bands up to 28 MHz may remain open throughout the day and night.

Sporadic E propagation

In addition to the main ionized layers there is also an irregular ionization effect which occurs at the height of the E layer. The effect is that a thin but intense ionized layer appears within the region of the E layer and this allows signals in the bands from 28–100 MHz to be reflected giving long-distance propagation at these frequencies. This effect is known as *sporadic E* propagation and occurs mainly during the summer months. This propagation mode can provide good DX results on 28 and 50 MHz bands.

Sunspot cycle

The general pattern of propagation on the HF bands is greatly influenced by the activity of the sun. Sunspots have been observed for many centuries and have been found to follow an eleven year cycle. When sunspot activity is at a maximum level the propagation on the higher frequency bands becomes extremely good since the upper layers of the atmosphere become heavily ionized. At the sunspot minimum the bands above about 15 MHz tend to be dead for long range operation although occasionally there will be brief openings during peaks of sunspot activity.

Critical frequency

The critical frequency (f_c) is the highest frequency at which a wave sent vertically up to the ionosphere is reflected by the E or F layer. The delay time between the transmitted pulse and the reflected echo gives a measure of the effective height of the layer (Figure 26).

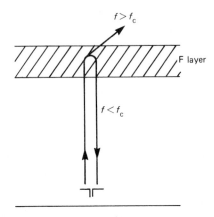

Figure 26 *Technique of ionospheric sounding used to find the critical frequency f_c and the height of the ionized layer*

Maximum usable frequency

When the space wave enters the ionosphere layer its path is bent as it travels through the layer. At the lower frequencies this bending action is quite rapid and the wave path is turned so that the wave is reflected back from the ionosphere and returns to earth. As the frequency is increased the amount of bending decreases and the wave penetrates deeper into the layer before being reflected. At higher frequencies the wave passes through the layer and goes on into space.

The highest frequency at which the wave is reflected from the ionosphere is known as the maximum usable frequency (MUF). To obtain a measure of the MUF it is normal to take ionospheric soundings to find the critical frequency f_c. The MUF is typically three times f_c for E layer reflection and five times f_c for the F layer.

Commercial circuits generally work at frequencies of about 0·85 of the MUF to ensure reliable communication and this frequency is known as the *optimum frequency*.

Skip distance

The simplest form of ionospheric propagation involves a single reflection from the ionized layer. The antenna radiates waves over a range of vertical angles so that the reflected wave returns to earth over a range of distances. At high vertical angles the signal may not be reflected giving a 'skip distance' where there is no reflected signal and the signals cannot be received (Figure 27). The 'skip distance' to the nearest point at which the reflected signal can be heard depends upon the height of the reflecting layer and the angle at which the transmitted signal is launched. For maximum distance the angle of radiation should be as low as possible.

A single hop transmission in which the signal is reflected only once from the E layer gives a maximum range of the order 2000 km. The higher F layer gives a single hop range up to 4000 km. Greater distances are possible by multiple hop propagation where the signal is reflected back and forth between the ionosphere and the ground. Each hop attenuates the signal but usable signals can be sent all the way around the earth via multiple hop propagation.

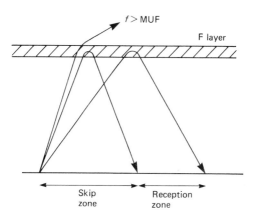

Figure 27 The 'skip zone' produced when radio waves are reflected from the ionosphere

HF band characteristics

1·8 MHz   Generally for local ground wave QSOs up to 100 miles during daylight. Can give good DX results late at night. Best at sunspot minimum.

3·5 MHz   Similar to 1·8 but giving greater daytime distance and good DX results after dark. Best at sunspot minimum.

7 MHz	Medium range during daylight up to perhaps 1000 miles with DX from dusk to dawn. Daytime results improve at sunspot maximum.
10 MHz	Similar to 7 MHz but tends to be better during daylight, dusk and dawn periods.
14 MHz	Primarily a daytime band with worldwide coverage particularly during sunspot maximum. The busiest amateur band for DX working at most times.
18 MHz	Similar to 14 MHz but tends to be poor during sunspot minimum.
21 MHz	When MUF is high this band provides worldwide DX and tends to be quieter than 14 MHz. Primarily a daylight band with signals falling off rapidly after dark.
24 MHz	Similar to 21 MHz.
28 MHz	Primarily a daylight band for DX operation when MUF is high. Allows excellent worldwide contacts with low power but conditions tend to be very variable. This band remains closed for DX most of the time during sunspot minimum.
50 MHz	This band tends to have mainly the characteristics of a VHF band but when MUF is high or during sporadic E periods it can provide very long range DX contacts.

Propagation beacons

In order to provide an indication of propagation conditions a number of beacon stations have been set up on the higher frequency HF bands. These are generally fairly low power stations operating continuously or on a time shared basis.

14 MHz beacons

The 14 MHz beacons were set up during World Communications Year (1983) by the Northern California DX Foundation (NCDXF). All operate on 14 100 kHz using A1A on a time shared basis. Each station operates in sequence for a period of one minute. In the first ten seconds the call sign is given in Morse. This is followed by nine second dashes with power levels of 100 W, 10 W, 1 W and 100 mW, in that order. The dashes are preceded by one, two, three or four dots to identify the power level. During the last ten seconds the station again identifies with its call sign in Morse. The sequence of beacons is as follows:

Minute	Call	Location
00	4U1UN/B	New York, USA
01	W6WX/B	Palo Alto, California, USA
02	KH60/B	Oahu Island, Hawaii
03	JA1IGY	Mt Asama, Japan
04	4X6TU/B	Tel Aviv, Israel
05	OH2B	Helsinki, Finland
06	CT3B	Madeira Island
07	ZS6DN/B	Transvaal, South Africa

The sequence starts on the hour with 4U1UN/B and cycles through in the order shown above with the cycle repeating every ten minutes. The last two minutes are reserved for two additional beacons in South America. There are plans to extend the coverage by adding further beacons in the future when the cycle time may be increased to 15 or 20 minutes.

21 MHz beacons

At the time of writing there are no beacons in this band but a series of time multiplexed beacons similar to those on 14 MHz is planned. These are expected to operate on a frequency of 21 150 kHz.

28 MHz beacons

In the band 28 200 to 28 300 there are a number of fixed frequency beacons operated by the various amateur organizations around the world. The operation of beacons in this band is currently under review and it is expected that in the future a number of time shared beacon networks similar to those on 14 MHz will be set up and the fixed frequency beacon system will be rationalized to provide a coordinated worldwide beacon system. Most of the currently operational 28 MHz beacons are low powered but they can provide a useful guide to the propagation conditions on this band.

Call	Frequency (MHz)	Location
A9XC	28·245	Bahrain
GB3SX	28·215	England
HG2BHA	28·2225	Hungary
LA5TEN	28·2375	Oslo, Norway
VE2TEN	28·2175	Quebec
VE3TEN	28·275	Ottawa
VE7TEN	28·2525	Vancouver
VK2WI	28·2625	Sydney
VK5WI	28·260	Adelaide
VP9BA	28·235	Bermuda
VS6HK	28·290	Hong Kong
VU2BCN	28·295	India
ZL2MHF	28·230	New Zealand
ZS1CTB	28·2425	Cape Town, South Africa
YV5AYV	28·280	Caracas, Venezuela
3B8MS	28·210	Mauritius

50 MHz beacons

Call	Frequency (MHz)	Location
FY7THF	50·039	French Guiana
GB3SIX	50·020	North Wales
H44HIR	50·005	Solomon Islands
KH6EQI	50·099	Hawaii
OX3VHF	50·045	Greenland
PY2AA	50·062	San Paulo, Brazil
TI2NA	50·080	Costa Rica
VS6HK	50·075	Hong Kong
VE1SIX	50·088	New Brunswick, Canada
VK8VF	52·200	Darwin, Australia
W3VD	50·062	Maryland, USA
ZB2VHF	50·035	Gibraltar
ZL2MHF	52·510	New Zealand
ZS6LN	50·098	Transvaal RSA
6Y5RC	50·025	Jamaica

Full lists of the 28 and 50 MHz beacons can be obtained from the RSGB.

VHF and UHF propagation

For frequencies above 50 MHz the sky wave is not normally reflected by the ionosphere even during a sunspot maximum period. Here the normal mode of propagation follows a simple line of sight path which is limited by the curvature of the earth's surface to the effective horizon distance. In practice the signal does extend some distance beyond the physical horizon but beyond this point the normal signal drops off very rapidly.

Radio horizon distance

For line of sight propagation the distance is limited by the curvature of the earth. The effective horizon distance for a VHF radio wave is slightly greater than the visual horizon distance because the wave path tends to be bent slightly by the atmosphere. By assuming an effective earth radius which is 1·33 times its actual value the radio horizon distance is given by:

$$D = 1·42\sqrt{H}$$

Where D is the horizon distance in miles and H is the antenna height above sea level in feet.

Tropospheric propagation

Long distance communication on VHF and UHF is possible due to propagation effects within the dense lower region of the atmosphere which is called the troposphere. An effect known as tropospheric 'ducting' can occur when a temperature inversion is present along the path between the two stations. Normally the temperature of the atmosphere falls with increasing height. In temperature inversion an upper layer of the atmosphere is at a higher temperature than the layer at ground level and this causes refraction of the VHF (Figure 28).

Tropospheric ducting can give propagation over hundreds of miles on 144 and 432 MHz. The effect usually occurs under high barometric pressure conditions in the early evening after a warm dry day particularly when there is fog or moist conditions at ground level. This mode tends to occur in the summer and autumn.

Diffraction effects

A ridge of hills or mountains can produce noticeable diffraction effects upon the VHF wave so that it is effectively bent to give reception beyond the ridge (Figure 29). The effect depends upon the angle at which the wave travels to the ridge and the sharpness of the edge of the ridge.

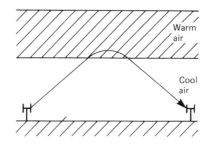

Figure 28   *Tropospheric propagation at VHF produced by refraction of the wave due to a temperature inversion in the atmosphere*

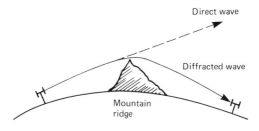

Figure 29   *Propagation of VHF signals over a mountain ridge by diffraction of the wavefront*

Aurora effects

An aurora is an electromagnetic storm occurring in the polar regions and accompanied by luminous displays in the sky (Figure 30). On the HF bands an aurora will usually cause disruption of communications due to severe static and fading problems. The auroral display causes heavy ionization of the atmosphere which can provide a reflective area for VHF and UHF signals allowing communications over long paths. The basic technique is that stations aim their beam antennas at the aurora from which the signal is reflected to the distant station. Since the ionization within the aurora changes rapidly auroral contacts are accompanied by fading and multipath distortion but can provide useful communications on 50 and 144 MHz using CW or SSB.

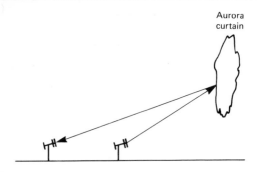

Figure 30 *VHF propagation produced by reflection of the wave from the ionized curtain produced by an auroral storm*

Propagation bulletins

Broadcast bulletins of current and forecast propagation conditions are transmitted as follows:

WWV Fort Collins, Colorado, USA
Frequencies   2·5, 5·0, 10·0, 15·0, 20·0 and 25·0 MHz

Bulletins are transmitted at fifteen minutes past each hour. Data given is the solar flux, A index, Boulder K index, solar activity and geomagnetic field conditions for the past twenty-four hours and predicted values for the next twenty-four hours. Announcement is in voice using AM.

Propagation conditions are also included in the ARRL news broadcast daily by W1AW and in the RSGB news broadcast on Sundays by GB2RS.

Solar flux
Solar flux is the measure of the radiation from the sun at 2800 MHz. A reading of 60 is a 'quiet' state. With readings over about 80 the higher HF bands (21 and 28 MHz) will open up for DX. Readings above 200 give twenty-four hour operation on 21 and 28 MHz and useful openings on 50 MHz.

A and K index
This is a measure of the earth's geomagnetic field. The A index is for a period of twenty-four hours and has a scale from 0 to 400. The K index is similar but uses a different scale and is updated more frequently. Low values of A or K index give best HF propagation. Higher values may indicate aurora conditions which may be useful for VHF operations.

Solar activity
This is an indication of rapid changes in solar flux and solar storms. It is indicated as low, medium, high or very high. High activity indicates propagation disturbance particularly on the HF bands.

Geomagnetic field conditions

This is usually quoted as quiet ($K < 1$), unsettled ($K = 1 - 3$) or active ($K > 3$). Best conditions are when the state is quiet since unsettled or active conditions indicate magnetic storms and probable HF blackout.

Meteor scatter propagation

One interesting mode of propagation that has been used by amateur stations is reflection from the ionized trail produced by a shower of meteors. During the year there are a number of showers of meteors which can provide meteor scatter contacts. Prominent showers are the Perseids in August and the Geminids in December. This mode of propagation may be used on the 50 and 144 MHz bands but can provide only brief contacts since the meteor trail will exist only for a short period of time.

8
Operating data

Call sign prefix allocations

A2A–A2Z	Botswana
A3A–A3Z	Tonga
A4A–A4Z	Oman
A5A–A5Z	Bhutan
A6A–A6Z	United Arab Emirates
A7A–A7Z	Qatar
A8A–A8Z	Liberia
A9A–A9Z	Bahrain
AAA–ALZ	USA
AMA–AOZ	Spain
APA–ASZ	Pakistan
ATA–AWZ	India
AXA–AXZ	Australia
AYA–AZZ	Argentina
BAA–BZZ	China
C2A–C2Z	Nauru
C3A–C3Z	Andorra
C4A–C4Z	Cyprus
C5A–C5Z	Gambia
C6A–C6Z	Bahamas
C7A–C7Z	World Meteorological Organization
C8A–C9Z	Mozambique
CAA–CEZ	Chile
CFA–CKZ	Canada
CLA–CMZ	Cuba
CNA–CNZ	Morocco
COA–COZ	Cuba
CPA–CPZ	Bolivia
CQA–CUZ	Portugal
CVA–CXZ	Uruguay
CYA–CZZ	Canada
D2A–D3Z	Angola
D4A–D4Z	Cape Verde Island
D5A–D5Z	Liberia
D6A–D6Z	Comoro Island
D7A–D9Z	South Korea
DAA–DRZ	West Germany
DSA–DRZ	South Korea
DUA–DZZ	Philippines
EAA–EHZ	Spain
EIA–EJZ	Eire
EKA–EKZ	USSR
ETA–ETZ	Ethiopia
EUA–EWZ	Byelorussia
EXA–EZZ	USSR
FAA–FZZ	France and dependencies
GAA–GZZ	UK
H2A–H2Z	Cyprus
H3A–H3Z	Panama
H4A–H4Z	Solomon Islands
H5A–H5Z	Botswana
H6A–H7Z	Nicaragua
H8A–H9Z	Panama
HAA–HAZ	Hungary
HBA–HBZ	Switzerland
HCA–HDZ	Ecuador
HEA–HEZ	Switzerland
HFA–HFZ	Poland
HGA–HGZ	Hungary
HHA–HHZ	Haiti
HIA–HIZ	Dominican Republic
HJA–HKZ	Colombia
HLA–HLZ	South Korea
HMA–HMZ	North Korea
HNA–HNZ	Iraq
HOA–HPZ	Panama
HQA–HRZ	Honduras
HSA–HSZ	Thailand
HTA–HTZ	Nicaragua
HUA–HUZ	Salvador
HVA–HVZ	Vatican
HWA–HYZ	France
HZA–HZZ	Saudi Arabia
IAA–IZZ	Italy
J2A–J2Z	Djibouti
J3A–J3Z	Grenada
J4A–J4Z	Greece
J5A–J5Z	Guinea-Bissau
J6A–J6Z	St Lucia
J7A–J7Z	Dominica
J8A–J8Z	St Vincent and Grenadines
JAA–JSZ	Japan
JTA–JVZ	Mongolia
JWA–JXZ	Norway
JYA–JYZ	Jordan
JZA–JZZ	Indonesia
KAA–KZZ	USA
L2A–L9Z	Argentina
LAA–LNZ	Norway

LOA–LWZ	Argentina
LXA–LXZ	Luxembourg
LYA–LYZ	USSR
LZA–LZZ	Bulgaria
MAA–MZZ	UK
NAA–NZZ	USA
OAA–OCZ	Peru
ODA–ODZ	Lebanon
OEA–OEZ	Austria
OFA–OJZ	Finland
OKA–OMZ	Czechoslovakia
ONA–OTZ	Belgium
OUA–OZZ	Denmark
P2A–P2Z	Papua New Guinea
P3A–P3Z	Cyprus
P4A–P4Z	Netherlands Antilles
P5A–P9Z	North Korea
PAA–PIZ	Netherlands
PJA–PJZ	Netherlands Antilles
PKA–POZ	Indonesia
PPA–PYZ	Brazil
PZA–PZZ	Surinam
RAA–RZZ	USSR
S2A–S3Z	Bangladesh
S6A–S6Z	Singapore
S7A–S7Z	Seychelles
S9A–S9Z	Sao Tomé and Principe
SAA–SMZ	Sweden
SNA–SRZ	Poland
SSA–SSM	Egypt
SSN–STZ	Sudan
SUA–SUZ	Egypt
SVA–SZZ	Greece
T2A–T2Z	Tuvalu
T3A–T3Z	Kiribati
T4A–T4Z	Cuba
T5A–T5Z	Somali Republic
T6A–T6Z	Afghanistan
T7A–T7Z	San Marino
TAA–TCZ	Turkey
TDA–TDZ	Guatemala
TEA–TEZ	Costa Rica
TFA–TFZ	Iceland
TGA–TGZ	Guatemala
THA–THZ	France
TIA–TIZ	Costa Rica
TJA–TJZ	Cameroon
TKA–TKZ	France
TLA–TLZ	Central African Republic
TMA–TMZ	France

TRA–TRZ	Gabon
TSA–TSZ	Tunisia
TTA–TTZ	Chad
TUA–TUZ	Ivory Coast
TVA–TXZ	France
TYA–TYZ	Benin
TZA–TZZ	Mali
UAA–UZZ	USSR
V2A–V2Z	Antigua
V3A–V3Z	Belize
V4A–V4Z	St Christopher— Nevis
V8A–V8Z	Brunei
VAA–VGZ	Canada
VHA–VNZ	Australia
VOA–VOZ	Canada
VPA–VSZ	UK
VTA–VWZ	India
VXA–VYZ	Canada
VZA–VZZ	Australia
WAA–WZZ	USA
XAA–XIZ	Mexico
XJA–XOZ	Canada
XPA–XPZ	Denmark
XQA–XRZ	Chile
XSA–XSZ	China
XTA–XTZ	Burkina Faso
XUA–XUZ	Campuchea
XVA–XVZ	Vietnam
XWA–XWZ	Laos
XXA–XXZ	Portugal
XYA–XZZ	Burma
Y2A–Y9Z	East Germany
YAA–YAZ	Afghanistan
YBA–YHZ	Indonesia
YIA–YIZ	Iraq
YJA–YJZ	Vanuatu
YKA–YKZ	Syria
YLA–YLZ	Latvia
YMA–YMZ	Turkey
YNA–YNZ	Nicaragua
YOA–YRZ	Rumania
YSA–YSZ	Salvador
YTA–YUZ	Yugoslavia
YVA–YYZ	Venezuela
YZA–YZZ	Yugoslavia
Z2A–Z2Z	Zimbabwe
ZAA–ZAZ	Albania
ZBA–ZJZ	UK
ZKA–ZMZ	New Zealand
ZNA–ZOZ	UK
ZPA–ZPZ	Paraguay
ZQA–ZQZ	UK
ZRA–ZUZ	South Africa
ZVA–ZZZ	Brazil

2AA–2ZZ	UK	6CA–6CZ	Syria
		6DA–6JZ	Mexico
3AA–3AZ	Monaco	6KA–6NZ	South Korea
3BA–3BZ	Mauritius	6OA–6OZ	Somali Republic
3CA–3CZ	Equatorial Guinea	6PA–6SZ	Pakistan
3DA–3DM	Swaziland	6TA–6UZ	Sudan
3DN–3DZ	Fiji	6VA–6WZ	Senegal
3EA–3FZ	Panama	6XA–6XZ	Madagascar
3GA–3GZ	Chile	6YA–6YZ	Jamaica
3HA–3UZ	China	6ZA–6ZZ	Liberia
3VA–3VZ	Tunisia		
3WA–3WZ	Vietnam	7AA–7IZ	Indonesia
3XA–3XZ	Guinea	7JA–7NZ	Japan
3YA–3YZ	Norway	7OA–7OZ	Yemen
3ZA–3ZZ	Poland	7PA–7PZ	Lesotho
		7QA–7QZ	Malawi
4AA–4CZ	Mexico	7RA–7RZ	Algeria
4DA–4IZ	Philippines	7SA–7SZ	Sweden
4JA–4LZ	USSR	7TA–7YZ	Algeria
4MA–4MZ	Venezuela	7ZA–7ZZ	Saudi Arabia
4NA–4OZ	Yugoslavia		
4PA–4SZ	Sri Lanka	8AA–8IZ	Indonesia
4TA–4TZ	Peru	8JA–8NZ	Japan
4UA–4UZ	United Nations	8OA–8OZ	Botswana
4VA–4VZ	Haiti	8PA–8PZ	Barbados
4WA–4WZ	Yemen	8QA–8QZ	Maldives
4XA–4XZ	Israel	8RA–8EZ	Guyana
4YA–4YZ	Civil Aviation	8SA–8SZ	Sweden
	(ICAO)	8TA–8YZ	India
4ZA–4ZZ	Israel	8ZA–8ZZ	Saudi Arabia
5AA–5AZ	Libya	9AA–9AZ	San Marino
5BA–5BZ	Cyprus	9BA–9DZ	Iran
5CA–5GZ	Morocco	9EA–9FZ	Ethiopia
5HA–5IZ	Tanzania	9GA–9GZ	Ghana
5JA–5KZ	Colombia	9HA–9HZ	Malta
5LA–5MZ	Liberia	9IA–9JZ	Zambia
5NA–5OZ	Nigeria	9KA–9KZ	Kuwait
5PA–5QZ	Denmark	9LA–9LZ	Sierra Leone
5RA–5SZ	Madagascar	9MA–9MZ	Malaysia
5TA–5TZ	Mauritania	9NA–9NZ	Nepal
5UA–5UZ	Niger	9OA–9TZ	Zaire
5VA–5VZ	Togo	9UA–9UZ	Burundi
5WA–5WZ	Western Samoa	9VA–9VZ	Singapore
5XA–5XZ	Uganda	9WA–9WZ	Malaysia
5YA–5ZZ	Kenya	9XA–9XZ	Ruanda
		9YA–9ZZ	Trinidad and
6AA–6BZ	Egypt		Tobago

List of countries

Country	Prefix	CQ zone	ITU zone
Afghanistan	YA	21	40
Aland Island	OHO	15	18
Alaska	AL7, KL7, NL7, WL7	1	2
Albania	ZA	15	28
Algeria	ZX	33	37
Amsterdam and St Paul Island	FB8Z	39	68
Andaman and Nicobar Islands	VU	26	49
Andorra	C3	14	27
Angola	D2	36	52
Antigua	V2A	8	11
Argentina	LU	13	14–16
Armenia	UG	21	29
Ascension Island	ZD8	36	66
Australia	VK1–3, VK5	30	59
	VK4	30	55
	VK6	29	58
	VK8	29	55
Austria	OE	15	28
Azerbaijan	UD	21	29
Azores	CT2	14	36
Bahamas	C6	8	11
Bahrain	A9X	21	39
Baker and Howland Islands	KH1	31	61
Balearic Islands	EA6	14	37
Bangladesh	S2	22	41
Barbados	8P	8	11
Belgium	ON	14	27
Belize	V3A	7	11
Benin	TY	35	46
Bermuda	VP9	5	11
Bhutan	A51	22	41
Bolivia	CP1, CP8, CP9	10	12
	CP2–CP7	10	14
Botswana	A22	38	57
Bouvet Island	3Y	38	67
Burkina Faso	XT	35	46
Brazil	PP1–5, PT2, PT9, PY1–5, PY9	11	15
	PP6–8, PR, PS, PT7	11	13
	PU, PV, PW, PY6–8	11	13
Brunei	VS5	28	54
Bulgaria	LZ	20	28
Burma	XZ	26	49
Burundi	9U5	36	52
Byelorussia	UC	16	29
Cameroon	TJ	36	46

Country	Prefix	CQ zone	ITU zone
Canada	VE1, VE2, VO	5	9
	VE3	4	4
	VE4, VE5	4	3
	VE6	4	2
	VE7	3	2
	VE8, VY1	1–2	2–5
Cape Verde Islands	D4C	35	46
Caroline Islands	KC6	27	64–65
Cayman Islands	ZF	8	11
Central African Republic	TL8	36	47
Chagos Islands	VQ9	39	41
Chile	CE1–CE5	12	14
	CE6–CE8	12	16
China	BV	23–24	43–44
Christmas Island	VK9X	29	54
Clipperton Islands	FO8	7	10
Cocos Islands	TI9	7	11
Colombia	HK	9	12
Comoro Islands	D68	39	53
Congo Republic	TN8	36	52
Cook Islands	ZK1	32	62
Corsica	FC	15	28
Costa Rica	TI	7	11
Crete	SV9	20	28
Cuba	CM, CO	8	11
Cyprus	5B4	20	39
Czechoslovakia	OK	15	28
Denmark	OZ	14	18
Djibouti	J28	37	48
Dominica	J73	8	11
Dominican Republic	HI	8	11
Easter Island	CEO	12	63
Ecuador	HC	10	12
Egypt	SU	34	38
Eire	EI, EJ	14	27
El Salvador	YS	7	11
Equatorial guinea	3C	36	47
Estonia	UR	15	29
Ethiopia	ET3	37	48
England	G, GB	14	27
Falkland Islands	VP8	13	16
Faroe Islands	OY	14	18
Fiji	3D2	32	56
Finland	OH	15	18
France	F, TK	14	27
Franz Josef Land	UA1	16	29
French Guiana	FY7	9	12
Gabon	TR8	36	52
Galapagos Islands	HC8	10	12
Gambia	C5A	35	46
Georgia	UF	21	29
Germany (East)	Y21 to Y99	14	28
Germany (West)	DA to DL	14	28

Country	Prefix	CQ zone	ITU zone
Ghana	9G1	35	46
Gibraltar	ZB2	14	37
Greece	SV	20	28
Greenland	OX	40	75
Grenada	J3	8	11
Guadeloupe	FG7	8	11
Guam	KH2	27	64
Guatemala	TG	7	11
Guernsey	GU, GB	14	27
Guinea	3X	35	46
Guinea-Bissau	J5	35	46
Guyana	8R	9	12
Haiti	HH	8	11
Hawaii	KH6	31	61
Heard Island	VK0	39	68
Honduras	HR	7	11
Hong Kong	VS6	24	44
Hungary	HA, HG	15	28
Iceland	TF	40	17
India	VU	22	41
Indonesia	YB, YC, YD	28	51, 54
Iran	EP	21	40
Iraq	YI	21	39
Isle of Man	GD, GB	14	27
Israel	4X, 4Z	20	39
Italy	I	15	28
Ivory Coast	TU2	35	46
Jamaica	6Y5	8	11
Jan Mayen Island	JX	40	18
Japan	JA–JR	25	45
Jersey	GJ, GB	14	27
Johnston Islands	KH3	31	61
Jordan	JY	20	39
Kazakhstan	UL7	17	30
Kenya	5Z4	37	48
Kerguelan Island	FB8X	39	68
Khmer Republic (Kampuchea)	XU	26	49
Kirghiz	UMB	17	30
Kiribati	T3	31	65
Korea	D7, HM	25	44
Kure Islands	KH7	31	61
Kuwait	9K2	21	39
Laos	XW8	26	49
Latvia	UQ	15	29
Lebanon	OD5	20	39
Lesotho	7P8	38	57
Liberia	EL, 5L	35	46
Libya	5A	34	38
Liechtenstein	HB0	14	28
Lithuania	UP	15	29
Luxembourg	LX	14	27
Macao	CR9	24	44
Madagascar	5R8	39	53

Country	Prefix	CQ zone	ITU zone
Madeira	CT3	33	36
Malawi	7Q7	37	53
Malaysia	9M	28	54
Maldives	8Q	22	41
Mali Republic	TZ	35	46
Malta	9H	15	28
Mariana Islands	KH0	27	64
Marshall Islands	KX6	31	65
Martinique	FM7	8	11
Mauritania	5T5	35	46
Mauritius	3B8	38	53
Mexico	XE	6	10
Midway Island	KH4	31	61
Moldavia	UO	16	29
Monaco	3A	15	27
Mongolia	JT	23	33
Morocco	CN	33	37
Mozambique	C9	37	53
Namibia	ZS3	38	57
Nauru	C21	31	65
Navassa Island	KP1	8	11
Nepal	9N1	22	42
Netherlands	PA, PD, PE, PI	14	27
Netherlands Antilles	PJ2, PJ3	9	12
	PJ4	9	11
	PJ5–8	8	11
New Caledonia	FK8	32	56
New Zealand	ZL	32	60
Nicaragua	HT	7	11
Niger Republic	5U7	35	46
Nigeria	5N	35	46
Niue	ZK2	32	62
Northern Ireland	GI, GB	14	27
Norway	LA–LJ	14	18
Oman	A4X	21	39
Pakistan	AP	21	41
Palmyra and Jarvis Island	KH5	31	61
Panama	HP	7	11
Papua New Guinea	P29	28	51
Paraguay	ZP	11	14
Peru	OA	10	12
Philippines	DU	27	50
Pitcairn Island	VR6	32	63
Poland	SP	15	28
Portugal	CS, CT	14	37
Puerto Rico	KP4	8	11
Qatar	A71	21	39
Reunion Island	FR7	39	53
Roumania	YO	20	28
RSFSR (Asia)	UA9	16–18	20, 21 30, 31
	UA0	18, 19	22–26 32–34

Country	Prefix	CQ zone	ITU zone
RSFSR (Europe)	UA, RA	16	19, 20 29, 30
	UA2, RA2	15	29
Rwanda	9X5	36	52
St Helena	ZD7	36	66
St Lucia	J6	8	11
St Martin	FS7	8	11
St Pierre and Miquelon	FP8	5	9
St Vincent	J88	8	11
Samoa	KH8	32	62
Samoa Western	SW1	32	62
San Marino	9A1	15	28
Sao Tomé and Principe	S92	36	47
Sardinia	IS0	15	28
Saudi Arabia	HZ	21	39
Scotland	GM, GB	14	27
Senegal	6W8	35	46
Seychelles	S79	39	53
Sierra Leone	9L1	35	46
Singapore	9V1	28	54
Solomon Islands	H44	28	51
Somali Republic	T5	37	48
South Africa	ZR, ZS	38	57
Spain	EA, EB, EC	14	37
Sri Lanka	4S7	22	41
Sudan	ST	34	47, 48
Surinam	PZ	9	12
Svalbard	JW	40	18
Swaziland	3D6	38	57
Sweden	SK, SL, SM	14	18
Switzerland	HB	14	28
Syria	YK1	20	39
Tadzhik	UJ	17	30
Taiwan	BV	24	44
Tanzania	5H3	37	53
Thailand	HS	26	49
Togo Republic	5V7	35	46
Tokelau Islands	ZM7	31	62
Tonga	A35	32	62
Trinidad and Tobago	9Y4	9	11
Tromelin Islands	FR7	39	53
Tunisia	3V8	33	37
Turkey	TA	20	39
Turkmen	UH	17	30
Turks and Caicos Islands	VP5	8	11
Tuvalu	T2	31	65
Uganda	5X5	37	48
Ukraine	UB5, UT5	15	29
United Arab Emirates	A6X	21	39
Uruguay	CX	13	14

Country	Prefix	CQ zone	ITU zone
USA	AA–AI, AJ, AK, K, N, W	3–5	6–8
Uzbek	UI	17	30
Vanuatu	YJ	30, 32	56
Vatican	HV	15	28
Venezuela	YV	9	12
Vietnam	XV	26	49
Virgin Islands	KP2	8	11
Wake Island	KH9	31	65
Wales	GW, GB	14	27
Wallis Islands	FW8	32	62
Western Samoa	5W1	32	62
Yemen Arab Republic	4W1	21	39
Yemen People's Republic	7O	21	39
Yugoslavia	YT, YU, YZ, 4N	15	28
Zaire	9Q5	36	52
Zambia	9J2	36	53
Zimbabwe	Z2	38	53

CQ DX zones

For the CQ worldwide DX contests organized by *CQ-TV Magazine* the world is divided up into a set of forty zones. These zones are also used for a special award known as the worked all zones (WAZ) award. The CQ worldwide zones are as follows:

1 Alaska KL7; Canada VY, VE8 (west of 102 W); Canada VE8 (east of 102 W)
2 Canada VE8 (east of 102 W) (parts of VE1 and VE2 north of 52N)
3 Canada BC; USA W6, W7 (Oregon, Washington, Idaho)
4 Canada VE3, VE4, VE5, VE6; USA W0, W5, W9, W7 (Wyoming, Montana)
5 Canada VE1, VE2, V0; Bermuda and FP8; USA W1, W2, W3, W4 (except Tennessee, Kentucky, Alabama); USA W8 (except Michigan, Ohio)
6 Mexico XE
7 Belize VP1; Costa Rica TI; Guatemala TG; Honduras HR; Nicaragua HT; Panama HP; Panama (US) KZ5; Salvador YS
8 Bahamas C6; Barbados 8P; Cayman Islands ZF; Cuba CO; Dominica J7; Dominican Republic HI; Grenada J5; Haiti HH; Guadeloupe FG; Jamaica 6Y; Leeward Island VP2; St Lucia J6; Martinique FM7; Puerto Rico KP4; Turks and Caicos Islands VP5; Netherland Antilles PJ5–8; Virgin Islands KV4; Windward Islands VP2
9 Colombia HK; French Guyana FY7; Guyana 8R; Surinam PZ; Trinidad and Tobago 9Y; Venezuela YV
10 Bolivia CP; Ecuador HC; Peru OA; Galapagos Islands HC8

11	Brazil PP–PY; Paraguay ZP
12	Chile CE
13	Argentina LU; Falkland Islands VP9; Uruguay CX
14	Andorra C3; Azores CT2; Balearic Islands EA6; Belgium ON; Denmark OZ; Eire EI; Faroes OY; France F; Holland PA; Germany (GFR) DL; Germany (DDR) Y2; Luxembourg LX; Monaco 3A; Norway LA; Spain EA; Sweden SM, Switzerland HB; UK G
15	Albania ZA; Austria OE; Corsica FC; Czechoslovakia OK; Estonia UR; Finland OH; Hungary HA; Italy I; Latvia UQ; Lithuania UP; Malta 9H; Russia UA2; San Marino 9A; Vatican HV; Yugoslavia YU
16	Moldavia UO; Ukraine UB5; Byelorussia UC2; Russia UA1, UA3, UA4, UA6, UA9S, UA9W
17	Kazakh UL; Kirghiz UM; Tadzhik UJ; Turkmen UH; Uzbek UI; Russia UA9
18	Russia UA9H, UA9O, UA9U, UA9Y, UA9Z, UA0A, UA0B, UA0H, UA0O, UA0S, UA0T, UA0V, UA0W
19	Russia UA0C, UA0D, UA0F, UA0I, UA0J, UA0S, UA0L, UA0O, UA0X, UA0Z
20	Bulgaria LZ; Cyprus 5B; Greece SV; Israel 4X; Jordan JY; Lebanon OD; Romania YO; Syria YK; Turkey TA
21	Afghanistan YA; Armenia UG; Azerbaijan UD; Bahrain A9; Georgia UF; Iran EP; Iraq YI; Kuwait 9K; Oman A4; Pakistan AP; Qatar A7; Saudi Arabia HZ; Yemen 4W; Yemen (PDR) 70; United Arab Emirates A8
22	Bangladesh S2; Bhutan A5; India VU; Maldives 8Q; Nepal 9N; SRI Lanka 4S
23	Mongolia JT; Russia UA0Y; Western China BV
24	Hong Kong VS6; Macao CR9; Taiwan BV; Eastern China
25	Japan JA, Korea
26	Burma XZ; Kampuchea XU; Laos XW; Thailand HS; Andaman and Nicobar Islands VU
27	Carolines KC6; Guam KH2; Marianas KH0; Philippines DU and nearby islands
28	Indonesia YC; Papua New Guinea P2; Sarawak 9M; Malaysia 9M; Singapore 9V; Solomon Islands H4
29	Australia VK6, VK8, VK9X, VK9Y
30	Australia VK1–5, VK7, VK9Z, VK0
31	Baker and Howland Islands KH1; Hawaii KH6; Jarvis Island KH5; Johnston Island KH3; Kiribati T3; Kure Island KH7; Marshall Island KX6; Midway Island KH4; Nauru C2; Tokelau Island ZM7; Tuvalu T2; Wake Island KW6
32	Fiji 3D; New Caledonia FK8; New Hebrides YJ; New Zealand ZL; Niue ZK2; Pitcairn Island VR6; American Samoa KH8; Tonga A3; Western Samoa 5W; Wallis and Futuna Islands FW8; Norfolk Island VK9
33	Algeria 7X; Canary Islands EA8; Madeira CT3; Morocco CN; Tunisia 3V; Ceuta-Melilla EA9
34	Egypt SU; Libya 5A; Sudan ST
35	Benin TY; Cape Verde D4; Gambia C5; Ghana 9G; Guinea 3X; Ivory Coast TU; Liberia EL; Mali TZ; Mauritania 5T; Niger 5U; Nigeria 5N; Senegal 6W; Sierra Leone 9L; Togo 5V; Bourkina Faso XT
36	Angola D2; Ascension ZD9; Burundi 9U; Cameroun TJ; Central African Republic TL; Chad TT; Congo TN; Equatorial Guinea 3C; Gabon TR; Rwanda 9X; St Helena ZD7; Sao Tomé and Principe S9; Zaire 9Q; Zambia 9J

37 Djibouti J2; Ethiopia ET; Kenya 5Z; Malawi 7Q; Mozambique C9; Somali Republic 6O; Uganda 5X
38 Botswana A2; Bouvet Island 3Y; Lesotho 7P; South Africa ZS; Swaziland 3D; Tristan da Cunha ZD9; Zimbabwe ZE
39 Chagos VQ9; Comoros D6; Heard Island VKO; Madagascar 5R; Mauritius 3B; Reunion FR7; Seychelles S7
40 Greenland OX; Iceland TF; Jan Mayen JX; Svalbard JW

International Telecommunication Union zones

An alternative zone scheme is used by the International Telecommunications Union (ITU).

1 Alaska KL7 (west of 141 W)
2 South-eastern Alaska KL7; Canada (south of 80 N, west of 110 W) VY, VE6, VE7, VE8
3 Canada VE4, VE5, VE8
4 Canada VE3, VE8 (70–90 W)
5 Canada VE8; Greenland OX
6 USA (west of 110 W) W6, W7
7 USA (from 90 W and 110 W) W4, W5, W7, W8, W9, W0
8 USA (east of 90 W) W1, W2, W3, W8, W9
9 Canada VE1, VE2, VO (south of 80 N); St Pierre and Miquelon FP8
10 Mexico XE; Clipperton Island FO8
11 Bahamas C6; Barbabos 8P; Belize VP1; Bermuda VP9; Cayman ZF; Costa Rica TI; Cuba CO; Dominica J7; Dominican Republic HI; Grenada J3; Guadeloupe FG7; Guatemala TG; Haiti HH; Honduras HR; Jamaica 6Y; Marinque FM7; Nicaragua HT; Panama Canal KZ6; Panama HP; Puerto Rico KP4; St Lucia J6; Salvador YS; Trinidad and Tobago 9Y; Virgin Islands KV4; Turks and Caicos VP5; Windward and Leeward Islands VP2; Netherlands Antilles PJ4–8
12 Bolivia (CP1, CP8–9); Columbia HK; Ecuador HC, French Guyana FY7; Guyana 8R; Peru OA; Surinam PZ; Venezuela YV; Netherlands Antilles PJ2–3
13 Brazil (PP6–8, PR, PS, PT7, PU, PV, PW, PY6–8, PY0)
14 Bolivia (CP2–7); Chile (CE1–5); Paraguay ZP; Uruguay CX; Argentina LU (north of 40 S)
15 Brazil (PP1, PP2, PT2, PY1–5)
16 Southern Argentina LU; Chile (CE6–8); Falklands Islands VP8
17 Iceland TF
18 Denmark OZ; Faroes OY; Finland OH; Jan Mayen JW; Norway LA; Sweden SM; Svalbard JX
19 Russia UA1N, UA1O, UA1Z, UN1
20 Russia UA1P, UA9J, UA9K, UA9X
21 Russia UA9L
22 Russia UA0A, UA0B, UA0H
23 Russia UA0Q
24 Russia UA0I (135 E–155 E)
25 Russia UA0X, UA0I (155 E–170 E)
26 Russia UA0I (170 E–170 W)
27 Andorra C3; Belgium ON; Eire EI; France F; Holland PA; Luxembourg LX; San Marino 3A; UK G, GD, GI, GJ, GM, GU, GW

28 Albania ZA; Austria OE; Bulgaria LZ; Corsica FC;
Czechoslovakia OK; Germany (FDR) DL; Germany (DDR)
Y2; Greece SV; Hungary HA; Italy I; Malta 9H; Poland SP;
Romania YO; Switzerland HB; Vatican HV; Yugoslavia YU
29 Armenia UG; Azerbaijan UD; Byelorussia UC; Estonia UR;
Georgia UF; Latvia UQ; Lithuania UP; Moldavia UO;
Ukraine UB5; Russia UA1–6 (south of 80 N and west of 50 E)
30 Kazakh UL; Turkmen UJ; Uzbek UI; Russia UA4H, UA4N,
UA4P, UA4W, UA9A, UA9C, UA9F, UA9G, UA9M, UA9Q,
UA9S, UA9W
31 Kirghiz UM; Russia UA9H, UA9O, UA9U, UA9Y, UA9Z
32 Mongolia JT (west of 110 E); Russia UA0O, UA0S, UA0T,
UA0W, UA0Y
33 Mongolia JT (east of 110 E), Russia UA0J, UA0U, UA0V
34 Russia UA0C, UA0D, UA0F, UA0L
35 Russia UA0Z
36 Azores CT2; Madeira CT3; Canary Islands EA8
37 Algeria 7X; Gibraltar ZB2; Morocco CN; Spain EA; Portugal
CT; Tunisia 3V
38 Egypt SU; Libya 5A
39 Bahrain A9; Cyprus 5B; Iraq YI; Israel 4X; Jordan JY; Kuwait
9K; Lebanon OD; Oman A4; Qatar A7; Syria YK; Saudi
Arabia HZ; Turkey TA; United Arab Emirates A6; Yemen 4W;
Yemen PDR 70
40 Afghanistan YA; Iran EP
41 Bangladesh S2; Bhutan A5; Chagos VQ9; India VU; Maldives
8Q; Pakistan AP; Sri Lanka 4S7
42 Nepal 9N
43 China B
44 Korea; Taiwan BV; Hong Kong VS6; Macao CR9
45 Japan JA
46 Benin TY; Bourkina Faso XT; Cameroun TJ; C. Verde D4;
Gambia C5; Ghana 9G; Guinea 3X; Guinea-Bissau J5; Ivory
Coast TU; Liberia EL; Mali TZ; Mauritania 5T; Niger 5U;
Nigeria 5N; Senegal 6W; Sierra Leone 9L; Togo 5V
47 Central African Republic TL; Chad TT; Equatorial Guinea 3C;
Sao Tomé and Principe S9; Sudan ST (west of 30 E)
48 Djibouti J2; Ethiopia ET; Kenya 5Z; Somali Republic 60;
Uganda 5X; Aldabra Island VQ9; Sudan ST (east of 30 E)
49 Burma XZ; Laos XW; Thailand HS; Kampuchea XU;
Andaman and Nicobar Islands VU
50 Philippines DU
51 Indonesia YC; Papua New Guinea P29; Solomon Islands H44
52 Angola D2
53 Comoros D6; Madagascar 5R; Malawi 7Q; Mauritius 3B;
Mozambique C9; Reunion Island FR7; Seychelles S7; Tanzania
5H; Zambia 9J; Zimbabwe ZE
54 Brunei V8; Malaysia 9M2; Sabah 9M6; Sarawak 9M8;
Singapore 9V; Christmas Island VK9X
55 Australia VK4, VK8, VK9Z
56 Fiji 3D; New Caledonia FK8; New Hebrides YJ
57 Botswana A2; Lesotho 7P; South Africa ZS; Swaziland 3D
58 Australia VK6
59 Australia VK1, VK2, VK3, VK5, VK7
60 Australia VK9, VK0; New Zealand ZL
61 Baker and Howland Island KH1; Hawaii KH6; Johnston Island
KH3; Kure Island KH7; Midway Island KH4; Palmyra Island
KH5
62 American Samoa KH8; Cook Island ZK1; Jarvis Island KP6,

WH5; Niue ZK2; Tokelau Island ZM7; Tonga A3; West Samoa 5W; Wallis and Futuna Island FW8
63   Marquesas Island FO8; Pitcairn Island VR6; Easter Island CE0A
64   Guam KH2; Marianas KH0; East Carolines KC6
65   Carolines KC6; Kiribati T3; Wake Island KH9; Nauru C21; Tuvalu T2; Marshall Island KX6
66   Ascension Island ZD8; Gough Island ZD9; St Helena ZD7
67   Antarctica OR4; Bouvet Island 3Y
68   Heard Island VK0, FB8X and FB8Z
69   Antarctica (40–100 E) VK0, 4K1
70   Antarctica (100–160 E) VK0, 4K1, KC4
71   Antarctica (160 E–140 W) ZL5
72   Antarctica (80–140 W) KC4
73   Antarctica (20–80 W) VP8, CE9, LU, KC4
74   South Pole KC4
75   Greenland OX; Arctic Canada VE8

The remaining ITU zones 76–89 cover sea areas only.

Call areas in the USA

In the USA the prefix number generally indicates the location of the station. Note that the assigned call prefix depends upon the state in which the station was initially licensed. Under new rules when a station moves to another call area the original call sign may be retained so that the prefix may not always indicate the current location of a station.

W1   Maine, Vermont, New Hampshire, Connecticut, Massachusetts, Rhode Island
W2   New York, New Jersey
W3   Pennsylvania, Delaware, Maryland
W4   Virginia, North Carolina, South Carolina, Georgia, Kentucky, Tennessee, Alabama, Florida
W5   Mississippi, Louisiana, Arkansas, Oklahoma, Texas, New Mexico
W6   California
W7   Washington, Oregon, Idaho, Montana, Wyoming, Nevada, Utah, Arizona
W8   Ohio, West Virginia
W9   Wisconsin, Illinois, Indiana
W0   North Dakota, South Dakota, Nebraska, Kansas, Minnesota, Iowa, Missouri, Colorado

Prefix letters may be W, K, N or AA–AL with the following exceptions:

AL7, KL7, NL7 and WL7 (Alaska)
KP, KV, NP and WP (Puerto Rico, Virgin Islands)
AH, KH, KX, NH and WH (Hawaii and other US islands)

Canadian call areas

VE1   New Brunswick, Nova Scotia, Prince Edward Island
VE2   Quebec
VE3   Ontario
VE4   Manitoba
VE5   Saskatchewan
VE6   Alberta
VE7   British Columbia
VE8   North West Territories
VY1   Yukon
VO1   Newfoundland
VO2   Labrador
VX9   Sable Island

Standard frequency transmissions

A number of standard frequency and time signal transmissions are available around the world. Most of these operate on frequencies of 5, 10, 15 and 20 MHz but some are on other special frequencies. The main stations are as follows with frequencies in kHz.

ATA	Delhi, India	5000, 10 000
BPM	Xi-an, China	10 000, 15 000
BSF	Taipei, Taiwan	5000, 15 000
CHU	Ottawa, Canada	3300, 7335, 14 670
FFH	Paris, France	2500
IAM	Rome, Italy	5000
JJY	Tokyo, Japan	2500, 5000, 10 000, 15 000
LOL	Buenos Aires, Argentina	5000, 10 000, 15 000
MSF	Rugby, England	60 kHz
RCH	Tashkent, USSR	2500, 5000, 10 000
RID	Irkutsk, USSR	5004, 10 004, 15 004
RTA	Novosibersk, USSR	10 000, 15 000
RWM	Moscow, USSR	4996, 9996, 14 996
VNG	Lyndhurst, Australia	4500, 7500, 12 000
WWV	Ft Collins, Col., USA	2500, 5000, 10 000, 15 000,
WWVH	Kauai, Hawaii	2500, 5000, 10 000, 15 000, 20 000
ZUO	Pretoria, South Africa	2500, 5000,

WWV transmissions (call signs of the National Bureau of standards time and frequency standard stations) include the time at every minute and also propagation bulletins at fifteen minutes past each hour. Time is given both in CW and as a voice message.

World time

Country		Winter	Summer
Afghanistan		$+4\frac{1}{2}$	$+4\frac{1}{2}$
Alaska		-10	-10
Albania		$+1$	$+1$
Algeria		GMT	GMT
Andaman and Nicobar Islands		$+5\frac{1}{2}$	$+5\frac{1}{2}$
Andorra		$+1$	$+1$
Angola		$+1$	$+1$
Argentina		-4	-3
Ascension Island		GMT	GMT
Australia	VK6	$+8$	$+8$
	VK5	$+9\frac{1}{2}$	$+10\frac{1}{2}$
	VK8	$+9\frac{1}{2}$	$+9\frac{1}{2}$
	VK1–3, VK7	-10	-11
	VK4	-10	-10
Austria		$+1$	$+2$
Azores		-1	GMT
Bahamas		-5	-4
Bahrain		$+4$	$+4$
Bangladesh		$+6$	$+6$
Barbados		-4	-4
Belgium		$+1$	$+2$
Belize		-6	-6
Benin		$+1$	$+1$
Bermuda		-4	-3
Bolivia		-4	-4
Botswana		$+2$	$+2$
Bourkina Faso		$+2$	$+3$
Brazil	East	-3	-3
	Central	-4	-4
	West	-5	-5
Brunei		$+8$	$+8$
Bulgaria		$+2$	$+3$
Burma		$+6\frac{1}{2}$	$+6\frac{1}{2}$
Burundi		$+2$	$+2$
Cameroon		$+1$	$+1$
Canada	VO	$-3\frac{1}{2}$	$-2\frac{1}{2}$
	VE1–2	-4	-3
	VE3	-5	-4
	VE4	-6	-5
	VE5–6	-7	-6
	VE7, VY	-8	-7
Cape Verde Islands		-2	-2
Cayman Islands		-5	-5
Central African Republic		$+1$	$+1$
Chad		$+1$	$+1$
Chagos Island		$+5$	$+5$
Chile		-4	-3
China		$+8$	$+8$
Christmas Island		$+7$	$+7$
Clipperton Islands		-7	-7
Colombia		-5	-5
Comoros Islands		$+3$	$+3$
Congo Republic		$+1$	$+1$
Cook Island		$-10\frac{1}{2}$	$-9\frac{1}{2}$
Costa Rica		-6	-6
Cuba		-5	-4
Cyprus		$+2$	$+3$
Czechoslovakia		$+1$	$+2$

Country		Winter	Summer
Denmark		$+1$	$+2$
Djibouti		$+3$	$+3$
Dominican Republic		-4	-4
Easter Island		-7	-6
Ecuador		-5	-5
Egypt		$+2$	$+3$
Eire		GMT	$+1$
El Salvador		-6	-6
Equatorial Guinea		$+1$	$+1$
Ethiopia		$+3$	$+3$
Falkland Islands		-4	-3
Faroe Islands		GMT	GMT
Fiji		$+12$	$+12$
Finland		$+2$	$+3$
France		$+1$	$+2$
Franz Josef Land		$+5$	$+5$
French Guiana		-3	-3
Gabon		$+1$	$+1$
Gambia		GMT	GMT
Germany (FDR and DDR)		$+1$	$+2$
Ghana		GMT	GMT
Gibraltar		$+1$	$+1$
Greece		$+2$	$+3$
Greenland		-3	-3
Guadeloupe		-4	-4
Guam		$+10$	$+10$
Guatemala		-6	-6
Guinea		GMT	GMT
Guinea-Bissau		-1	-1
Guyana		$-3\frac{3}{4}$	$-3\frac{3}{4}$
Haiti		-5	-5
Hawaii		-10	-10
Honduras		-5	-6
Hong Kong		$+8$	$+9$
Hungary		$+1$	$+2$
Iceland		-1	GMT
India		$+5\frac{1}{2}$	$+5\frac{1}{2}$
Indonesia	West	$+7$	$+7$
	Central	$+8$	$+8$
	East	$+9$	$+9$
Iran		$+3\frac{1}{2}$	$+4\frac{1}{2}$
Iraq		$+3$	$+3$
Israel		$+2$	$+2$
Italy		$+1$	$+2$
Ivory Coast		GMT	GMT
Jamaica		-5	-4
Jan Mayen Island		-1	-1
Japan		$+9$	$+9$
Johnston Islands		-10	-10
Jordan		$+2$	$+2$
Kenya		$+3$	$+3$
Kerguelen Islands		$+5$	$+5$
Khmer Republic (Kampuchea)		$+7$	$+7$
Kiribati		$+12$	$+12$
Korea		$+9$	$+9$
Kuwait		$+3$	$+3$
Laos		$+7$	$+7$
Lebanon		$+2$	$+2$
Leeward Island		-4	-4
Lesotho		$+2$	$+2$
Liberia		GMT	GMT
Libya		$+2$	$+2$
Luxembourg		$+1$	$+2$

Country	Winter	Summer
Macao	+8	+8
Madagascar	+3	+3
Madeira	GMT	GMT
Malawi	+2	+2
Malaysia West	+7½	+7½
East	+8	+8
Maldives	+5	+5
Mali Republic	GMT	GMT
Malta	+1	+2
Mariana Islands	+10	+10
Marshall Islands	+12	+12
Mauritania	GMT	GMT
Mauritius	−4	−4
Mexico East	−6	−6
West	−7	−7
Midway Island	−11	−11
Monaco	+1	+2
Mongolia	+8	+8
Morocco	GMT	GMT
Mozambique	+2	+2
Nauru	+12	+12
Nepal	+5⅔	+5⅔
Netherlands (Holland)	+1	+2
Netherlands Antilles	−4	−4
New Caledonia	+11	+11
New Zealand	+12	+13
Nicaragua	−6	−6
Niger Republic	+1	+1
Nigeria	+1	+1
Niue	−11	−11
Norway	+1	+2
Oman	+4	+4
Pakistan	+5	+5
Panama	−5	−5
Papua New Guinea	+10	+10
Paraguay	−4	−3
Peru	−5	−5
Philippines	+8	+8
Pitcairn Island	−8½	−8½
Poland	+1	+2
Portugal	GMT	+1
Puerto Rico	−4	−4
Qatar	+4	+4
Reunion Island	+4	+4
Roumania	+2	+3
Russia Moscow	+3	+4
Sverdlovsk	+5	+6
Tomsk	+7	+8
Irkutsk	+8	+9
Yakutsk	+9	+10
Vladivostok	+10	+11
Magadan	+11	+12
Rwanda	+2	+2
St Helena	GMT	GMT
St Pierre and Miquelon	−4	−4
Samoa	−11	−11
Sao Tomé and Principe	GMT	GMT
Saudi Arabia	+3	+3
Senegal	GMT	GMT
Seychelles	+4	+4
Sierra Leone	GMT	GMT
Singapore	+7½	+7½
Solomon Islands	+11	+11

Country	Winter	Summer
Somali Republic	+3	+3
South Africa	+2	+2
Spain	+1	+2
Sri Lanka	+5½	+5½
Sudan	+2	+2
Suriname	−3½	−3½
Swaziland	+2	+2
Sweden	+1	+2
Switzerland	+1	+2
Syria	+2	+2
Taiwan	+8	+8
Tanzania	+3	+3
Thailand	+7	+7
Togo Republic	GMT	GMT
Tokelau Islands	−11	−11
Tonga	+13	+13
Trinidad	−4	−4
Tunisia	+1	+1
Turkey	+2	+2
Turks and Caicos Islands	−5	−4
Tuvalu	+12	+12
Uganda	+3	+3
United Arab Emirates	+4	+4
UK	GMT	+1
Uruguay	−3	−3
USA Eastern	−5	−4
Central	−6	−5
Mountain	−7	−6
Pacific	−8	−7
Vanuatu	+11	+11
Venezuela	−4	−4
Vietnam	+7	+7
Virgin Islands	−4	−4
Wake Island	+12	+12
Yemen	+3	+3
Yugoslavia	+1	+1
Zaire East	+2	+2
West	+1	+1
Zambia	+2	+2
Zimbabwe	+2	+2

Time signal stations

Argentina	LOL 5000, 10 000, 15 000 kHz
	LQB9 8167·5, 17 550 kHz
Australia	VNG 4500, 7500, 12 000 kHz
Brazil	PPE 8721 kHz
Canada	CHU 3330, 7335, 14 670 kHz
China	BPV 5000, 10 000, 15 000 kHz
Czechoslovakia	OMA 2500, 3170 kHz
Ecuador	HD2IOA 3810, 5000, 7600 kHz
France	FFH 2500 kHz
	FTH42 7428 kHz

Germany	DAN 2614 kHz
	DAO 2775 kHz
	DIZ 4525 kHz
Guam	NPN 4955, 8150, 13 380 kHz
Hong Kong	VPS 35, 8539, 13 020 kHz
India	VWC 12 745 kHz
Italy	IBF 5000 kHz
Japan	JJY 5000, 10 000, 15 000 kHz
Spain	EBC 12 008 kHz
USA	WWV 5000, 10 000, 15 000, 20 000 kHz
USSR	RWM 4996, 9996, 14 996 kHz
Venezuela	YVTO 6100 kHz

Signal reporting codes

QRK, QSA and QRI
Signal readability:

QRK1   Bad
QRK2   Poor
QRK3   Fair
QRK4   Good
QRK5   Excellent

Signal strength:

QSA1   Barely audible
QSA2   Weak
QSA3   Fairly good
QSA4   Good
QSA5   Very good

Signal tone:

QRI1   Good
QRI2   Variable
QRI3   Bad

RST code
This code is generally used by amateur stations for reporting on the
reception conditions of the received signal. The code consists of three
digits representing readability (R), signal strength (S) and tone (T).
For voice transmissions only the R and S parts of the code are used.
The code meanings are as follows:

Readability:

R1   Unreadable
R2   Barely readable
R3   Readable with difficulty
R4   Good readability
R5   Perfectly readable

Signal strength:

S1   Barely audible
S2   Very weak
S3   Weak

S4 Fair
S5 Fairly good
S6 Good
S7 Moderately strong
S8 Strong
S9 Extremely strong

Tone:

T1 Extremely rough hissing note
T2 Very rough AC note, not musical
T3 Rough low pitched AC note
T4 Rather rough AC note, musical
T5 Musically modulated tone
T6 Modulated tone, slight whistle
T7 Near DC tone, smooth ripple
T8 Good DC tone
T9 Pure DC tone

A good signal with excellent tone and readability would be reported as RST579. For telephony contacts only the R and S parts of the code are used so a typical report might be R5, S8. For some reports signal strengths of S9 + a number of dBs may be given. These are based on readings from typical receiver S meters which are usually calibrated up to S9 + 60 dB. An S point in the range 1 to 9 is usually taken as being approximately 6 dB.

SINPO code

A more comprehensive reporting code is the SINPO code which gives readings for S (signal strength), I (interference), N (noise—static), P (propagation disturbance—fading) and O (overall reception quality). The ratings are as follows:

Strength (S):

1 Barely audible
2 Poor
3 Fair
4 Good
5 Excellent

Interference (I):

1 Extreme
2 Severe
3 Moderate
4 Slight
5 None

Noise (N):

1 Extreme
2 Severe
3 Moderate
4 Slight
5 None

Propagation disturbance – fading (P):

1 Extreme
2 Severe
3 Moderate
4 Slight
5 None

Overall rating (O):

1   Unusable
2   Poor
3   Fair
4   Good
5   Excellent

The report consists of the word SINPO followed by a string of five numbers. If any of the parameters is not reported its number is substituted by the letter X.

SINPFEMO code

The SINPFEMO reporting code is similar to the SINPO code but provides more information since it includes additional reports on F (frequency of fading), E (modulation quality) and M (modulation depth). The SINPO parts of the code are identical to those for a SINPO report and the additional parameters are as follows:

Frequency of fading (F):

1   None
2   Slow
3   Moderate
4   Fast
5   Very fast

Modulation quality (E):

1   Very poor
2   Poor
3   Fair
4   Good
5   Excellent

Modulation depth (M):

1   Continuously overmodulated
2   Poor or no modulation
3   Fair
4   Good
5   Excellent

Here the code is sent as for SINPO by sending the letters SINPFEMO followed by eight numbers with an X inserted for any parameter not reported.

Amateur radio abbreviations

ABT	About
AGN	Again

ANI	Any
ANT	Antenna
ATU	Antenna tuner unit
BCNU	Be seeing you
BK	Break in
BURO	QSL bureau
CONDX	Propagation conditions
CPY	Copy
CQ	General call
CU	See you
CUAGN	See you again
CUL	See you later
DX	Long distance or difficult contact
ES	And
FB	Fine business
GB	Goodbye
GD	Good
GE	Good evening
GM	Good morning
GN	Good night
HAM	Radio amateur
HI	Laughter
HR	Here
HPE	Hope
HW	How
MNI	Many
NR	Number or near
NW	Now
OB	Old boy
OM	Old man
OT	Old timer
PSE	Please
R	Roger (all received OK)
RIG	Transmitter and receiver
RPT	Report
RX	Receiver
SIGS	Signals
SKED	Schedule
TCVR	Transceiver
TKS	Thanks
TNX	Thanks
TU	Thank you
Tx	Transmitter
U	You
UR	You are
VY	Very
WDS	Words
WKG	Working
WX	Weather
XTAL	Quartz crystal
XYL	Wife
YL	Young lady
YR	Your
73	Best wishes
88	Love and kisses

Phonetic alphabet

To ensure correct reception of important information when using
telephony the key words may be spelled out using phonetic words to
represent each letter of the word being spelled. Many different
phonetic alphabets have been used but the recommended one for
general use by amateurs is the one adopted by the International Civil
Aviation Organization (ICAO) which is as follows:

Letter	Code word	Pronunciation
A	Alpha	AL fah
B	Bravo	BRAH voh
C	Charlie	CHAR lee
D	Delta	DELL tah
E	Echo	ECK oh
F	Foxtrot	FOKS trot
G	Golf	GOLF
H	Hotel	hoh TELL
I	India	IN dee ah
J	Juliet	JEW lee ET
K	Kilo	KEE loh
L	Lima	LEE mah
M	Mike	Mike
N	November	No VEM ber
O	Oscar	OSS cah
P	Papa	PAH pah
Q	Quebec	Keh BECK
R	Romeo	ROW me oh
S	Sierra	See AIR ra
T	Tango	TANG go
U	Uniform	YOU nee form
V	Victor	VIK tah
W	Whiskey	WISS key
X	X-ray	ECKS ray
Y	Yankee	YANG key
Z	Zulu	ZOO loo

Capital letters denote a stressed syllable.

Phonetic figures

Figure	Word	Pronunciation
0	NADAZERO	nah dah zay roh
1	UNAONE	oo nah wun
2	BISSOTWO	bees soh too
3	TERRATHREE	tay rah tree
4	KARTEFOUR	kar tay fower
5	PANTAFIVE	pan tah five

6	SOXISIX	sok see six
7	SETTESEVEN	set tay seven
8	OKTOEIGHT	ok toh ait
9	NOVENINE	no vay niner
.	DECIMAL	day see mal

All syllables are equally stressed.

Q code

The Q code was introduced primarily for telegraphy using Morse and consists of a series of three letter codes which have specific meanings and enable a relatively long message to be conveyed rapidly. Many of the Q code groups are used by radio amateurs to save time and may be used both for telegraphy and telephony contacts. If a query symbol is sent after the code it indicates a question whereas the Q code by itself indicates a reply. An example is:

QTH?   What is your location?
QTH   My location is . . .

The series of codes from QAA to QIZ and QKA to QOT are used for messages relating to aircraft operations and are not listed here.

The codes from QJA to QJZ are used for automatic telegraphy operations.

QRA   The name of my station is . . .
QRB   The distance between our stations is . . .
QRE   My estimated time of arrival is . . .
QRF   I am returning to . . .
QRG   Your exact frequency is . . .
QRH   Your frequency varies
QRI   The tone of your signals is . . .
    1   Good
    2   Variable
    3   Bad
QRK   Your signal readability is . . .
    1   Bad
    2   Poor
    3   Fair
    4   Good
    5   Excellent
QRL   The frequency is in use
QRM   I am being interfered with
QRN   The channel is noisy (Static)
QRO   Increase transmitter power
QRP   Reduce transmitter power
QRQ   Send faster
QRS   Send slower
QRT   Stop sending
QRU   I have nothing for you
QRV   I am ready
QRW   Please inform . . . that I am calling his station
       on . . . kHz

QRY	Your turn is number ...
QRZ	You are being called by ...
QSA	Your signal strength is ...
	1 Barely audible
	2 Weak
	3 Fairly good
	4 Good
	5 Very good
QSB	Your signals are fading
QSC	I am a cargo vessel
QSD	Your keying is defective
QSI	I have been unable to break in
QSK	I can hear you between my signals. Break in
QSL	I am acknowledging receipt
QSM	Repeat your last message
QSN	I did hear you on ... kHz
QSO	I can communicate with ... direct
QSP	I will relay your message to ...
QSR	Repeat your call on the calling frequency
QSS	I will use the working frequency ...
QSU	Send or reply on this frequency
QSV	Send a series of Vs
QSW	I am going to send on this frequency
QSX	I am listening to ... on ... kHz
QSY	Change frequency to ... kHz
QSZ	Send each word or group twice.

The QTA to QUZ codes are intended for search and rescue functions but the following are useful in amateur radio:

QTH	My position is ...
QTR	The correct time is ...
QTS	I will send my call sign for tuning or frequency measurement purposes
QTX	I will keep my station open until ...
QUA	Here is news of ...
QUB	Here is the information requested ...
QUM	Normal working may be resumed

QTH locator systems

For most amateur contacts, particularly on the HF bands the location of the station is usually given by referring to the geographical location or the nearest large town or city. For VHF and UHF operation a more precise location reference is often needed particularly for contest operation. Two systems have been used for this purpose.

The Maidenhead worldwide system
In recent years a new locator system has been introduced which provides location codes for worldwide use. This is generally known as the *Maidenhead system* and has replaced the earlier European system.

The entire world surface is divided up into a matrix of large areas each of which is 10° of longitude by 20° of latitude (Figure 31). Each area is identified by a two-letter code with the first letter indicating longitude position and the second representing latitude position. The longitude letter starts at 180° west with letter **A** and ends with letter **R** which extends to 180° East. For north–south position the codes start with **A** at the south pole and progress northwards to letter **R** which extends to the north pole.

Each major area is divided into 100 smaller areas arranged as a 10 by 10 matrix (Figure 32). Here a two-digit number code is used with the first digit giving the east–west position and the second digit giving the north–south position. These areas are 2° of longitude wide and 1° of latitude high.

Each of these secondary areas is divided into a final matrix of 24 by 24 small segments (Figure 33), each of which is defined by a final two-letter code using letters from A to X. This final code defines an area of five minutes of longitude by 2.5 minutes of latitude.

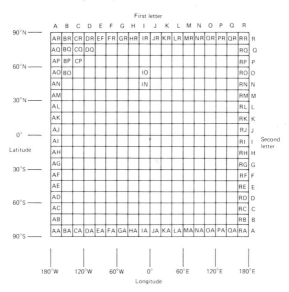

Figure 31   *Division of the earth's surface into major areas for the Maidenhead locator system*

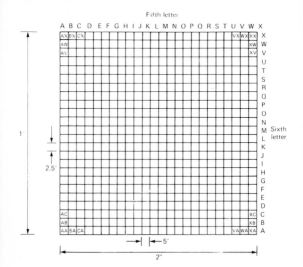

Figure 32 *Division of the major locator areas to give the second pair of symbols for the locator code*

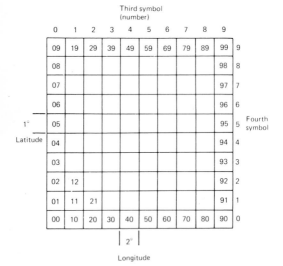

Figure 33 *Division of the minor locator areas to give a more precise locator code with six symbols*

9
Amateur radio news bulletins

RSGB news bulletin

Transmitted each week on Sunday at the following times:

3650 kHz (SSB) 0900, 0930, 1000, 1030, 1100, 1800, 3640 and
   3640 and 3660 kHz (SSB) 1130
7047 kHz (AM) 0900, 1100
144·250 MHz (SSB) 0930, 1000, 1030, 1100, 1130
144·525 MHz (FM) 0930, 1000, 1030, 1100, 1130

   The news is also relayed through some 432 MHz repeaters and has
been transmitted via amateur satellites during passes over Britain.

ARRL news bulletins

The ARRL transmits daily news bulletins from station W1AW at
Newington, Connecticut, USA. These include propagation forecasts
and are transmitted using CW, SSB and RTTY modes. Special
emergency bulletins may be transmitted on the hour for SSB, at
fifteen minutes past the hour for RTTY and on the half hour for CW
using the same frequencies as the regular bulletins.

CW bulletins (eighteen words per minute)
Frequencies: 3580, 7080, 14 070, 21 080, 28 080 kHz
Daily at: 0100, 0400 and 2200 GMT
Monday to Friday also at 1500 GMT

   During the summer months when local daylight time is in
operation the transmissions are one hour earlier.

Voice bulletins using SSB

Frequencies: 3990, 7290, 14 290, 21 390, 28 590, 50 190 kHz
Daily at: 0230 and 0530 GMT

   In summer these times are one hour earlier.

RTTY bulletins
The bulletin is sent first at 45 baud using Baudot code then repeated
using ASCII code at 110 baud and finally transmitted at 100 baud
using FEC (mode B AMTOR).

Frequencies: 3625, 7095, 14 095, 21 095 and 28 095 kHz
Daily at: 0200, 0500 and 2300 GMT
Monday to Friday also at 1600 GMT
   In the summer these times are one hour earlier.

P14AA news bulletins

The Dutch amateur radio organization VERON provides weekly
bulletins of DX news. These bulletins are broadcast on Fridays at the
following times:

Telephony (SSB)
1830 GMT   Amateur radio news in Dutch
1845 GMT   DX news in English
2030 GMT   News in Dutch
2045 GMT   News in English

RTTY bulletin
Transmitted first in Baudot (50 baud) then repeated in AMTOR
Mode B (FEC)
2000 GMT   DX news in Dutch
2015 GMT   DX news in English

Frequencies: 3602 kHz, 14 103 kHz, 144·80 MHz (FM)

10
Antennas

For any transmitting or receiving system a most important element is
the antenna which radiates or picks up the electromagnetic waves.
Although any random piece of wire will act as an antenna, most
types of antenna used by amateurs are made to resonate at the
frequency band in use.

Antenna impedance

All antennas exhibit an impedance at their feed point. The resistive
part of this impedance is the *radiation resistance*. In a resonant
antenna such as a dipole the impedance will be the radiation
resistance. For non-resonant antennas the impedance contains a
capacitive or inductive component as well as resistance. For optimum
transfer of power from the transmitter to the antenna the output
impedance of the transmitter should be matched to the impedance of
the antenna that it is driving. In most cases a matching circuit, known
generally as the antenna tuning unit (ATU) is inserted between the
transmitter and the antenna. Transmitter output impedance for a
modern transceiver is generally arranged to be 50 Ω and is purely
resistive. The ATU is used to cancel out any reactive components of
the antenna impedance and to match the resistive component to the
50 Ω transmitter output.

Polar diagram

Most types of aerial do not radiate equally in all directions and the
polar diagram shows the radiation pattern of the antenna (Figure 34).
The polar diagram which is usually of interest is the plan view which
shows the pattern of radiation around the antenna in the horizontal
plane.

For a directional beam antenna the radiation is primarily in one
direction and there is virtually no radiation from the sides and back
of the antenna. Any small areas of signal at the sides and back of the
radiation pattern are referred to as side lobes. In the design of a
directional antenna the object is to reduce these to the smallest
possible size.

The beam width is the angular width of the main lobe at the point
where the radiation power is reduced by 3 dB relative to the
maximum power point at the centre of the main lobe.

The ratio between the power in the forward direction of the
antenna to that from the rear is referred to as the *front to back ratio* of
the antenna. Antenna design is usually a compromise between
achieving high forward gain with a narrow beam width and retaining
a high front to back ratio.

A second polar diagram may be produced which gives the
radiation pattern in the vertical plane.

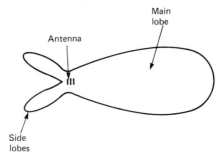

Figure 34 *Polar diagram showing the directional properties of a beam antenna*

Antenna polarization

If a wire antenna such as a dipole is mounted horizontally the electric field of the radiated wave is in the horizontal plane and the magnetic field is vertical. This produces a horizontally polarized wave.

A vertically polarized wave is one in which the electric component of the wave field is in the vertical plane and the magnetic component is in the horizontal plane. This type of polarization is produced by a vertical wire antenna such as a Marconi or ground plane type.

An antenna which is sloping produces a mixture of both horizontal and vertically polarized waves.

It is possible to produce circularly polarized waves by feeding crossed antennas (one horizontal and one vertical) with signals that are 90° out of phase. This type of polarization is often used at VHF and UHF and for satellite antennas.

Isotropic aerial

This is a theoretical antenna which radiates equally in all directions. It is often used as a reference when quoting the gain of an antenna.

Antenna gain

The effective gain of the antenna is the ratio between the radiated power in the direction of maximum radiation of the antenna compared with the radiated power from an isotropic antenna fed with the same input power. A simple dipole gives a gain of the order 2 dB over an isotropic radiator. In some cases gain is referred to a half wave dipole which gives gain figures about 2 dB lower than those based upon an isotropic antenna.

The dipole

Probably the most widely used antenna is the centre fed dipole or doublet type which is shown in Figure 35. The dipole length is theoretically half a wavelength at the frequency being used and the RF signal is fed to the centre of the antenna which has a typical input impedance of about 72 Ω. For HF antennas which are mounted close to the ground the impedance will generally be lower than the theoretical value.

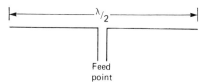

Figure 35   *The half wave doublet or dipole antenna*

The formula for calculating the length of a dipole is

$$\text{Length} = \frac{150}{f} \text{ m or } \frac{492}{f} \text{ ft}$$

Where f is the frequency in MHz.

For HF antennas the length should be reduced by about 5 per cent for proper resonance so the length formula becomes:

$$\text{Length} = \frac{143}{f} \text{ m or } \frac{468}{f} \text{ ft}$$

If the dipole is mounted with the elements horizontal the radiation pattern is a figure of eight shape with maximum signal broadside to the antenna and minimum signal off the ends of the antenna (Figure 36). If the dipole is mounted vertically the radiation pattern is equal in all directions in the horizontal plane (Figure 37). A vertical dipole is said to be *omnidirectional*.

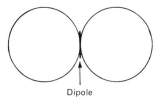

Figure 36   *Polar radiation diagram for a horizontal dipole antenna*

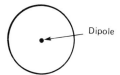

Figure 37   *Polar radiation diagram for a vertical dipole antenna*

Folded dipole

A variation of the simple dipole is the folded dipole which has a second element connected between the ends of the dipole (Figure 38). The effect of this extra element is to increase the antenna feed impedance to approximately 288 Ω. The radiation pattern and dipole length are the same as for a normal dipole.

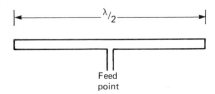

Figure 38   *The folded dipole antenna*

Multiband dipole antenna

A simple dipole will work effectively only on the band for which it is designed. For amateur use where several different bands are to be used a separate dipole could be used for each band with separate feeder cables for each dipole. A simpler scheme is to connect the dipoles for several bands in parallel at their feed point and use a single feeder cable (Figure 39). The dipole elements are fanned out from the feed point to reduce interaction between individual dipoles. This scheme relies on the fact that dipoles for bands other than the one in use will exhibit high active impedances so that most of the power is delivered to the dipole for the band in use. In practice the presence of the other dipoles causes some detuning of the dipole in use so the lengths of the dipoles will usually need to be adjusted slightly by trial and error to attain proper resonance on each operating band. Once set up this type of antenna can provide effective multiband working with no need to switch antenna feeders when changing bands.

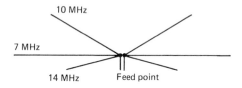

Figure 39   *A multiband antenna using dipoles connected in parallel*

The trap dipole

An alternative method of producing a multiband dipole antenna system makes use of tuned trap circuits inserted into the dipole elements (Figure 40). The traps are tuned circuits which act as rejectors for the higher frequency bands and effectively isolate sections of the antenna when the higher bands are being used. In the example shown the centre part of the antenna between the two traps is effectively a 28 MHz dipole. If the traps are tuned to 28 MHz they present a very high impedance and effectively isolate the rest of the antenna. When the antenna is used on 14 MHz the trap circuits are no longer resonant and present a low impedance thus allowing the full antenna length to become operational as a 14 MHz dipole. Trap dipole antennas can readily be built to cover three or four HF amateur bands.

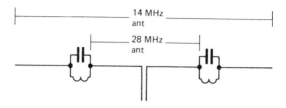

Figure 40 *A multiband antenna using traps to isolate the sections according to the band in use*

Marconi antenna

An alternative type of antenna to the dipole is the Marconi which is a vertical wire or tower of approximately a quarter of a wavelength for the band in use. The signal is applied between the bottom of the antenna and ground (Figure 41). This antenna produces vertically polarized signals and has a typical impedance of about 30 to 35 Ω. The radiation pattern is omnidirectional in the horizontal plane.

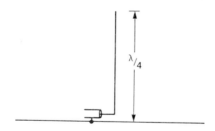

Figure 41 *Marconi type quarter wave vertical antenna*

Ground plane aerial

The ground plane antenna is basically a quarter wave vertical Marconi type antenna with its own ground plane screen. Thus although the antenna may be mounted high above actual ground it operates against its own ground plane. The ground plane may be a metal sheet approximately half a wavelength in diameter or more commonly it consists of a number of radial elements which have a length of about a quarter wavelength (Figure 42).

The ground plane antenna has the advantage that it produces a low vertical angle of radiation compared with say a vertical dipole and has a typical main lobe at around 30 degrees above the ground plane (Figure 43). Feed impedance is nominally about $35\,\Omega$ and the feed is unbalanced so the ground plane antenna is normally fed by a coaxial feeder cable.

By setting the radials so that they slope downwards at an angle of around $45°$ (Figure 44), the feed impedance can be increased to the order of $50\,\Omega$ which provides a convenient match for many feeder cables and transmitter outputs.

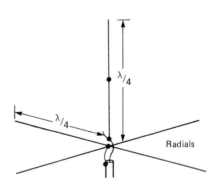

Figure 42   *Ground plane antenna with four quarter wave radials*

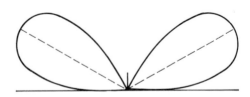

Figure 43   *Radiation pattern in the vertical plane for a Marconi or ground plane type antenna*

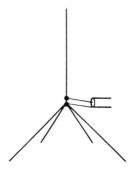

Figure 44   *A ground plane antenna with its radials drooped at a 45°*
angle to give 50 Ω impedance match

Loaded vertical antennas

If the length of a vertical antenna is increased to 5/8 wavelength the
input resistance becomes approximately 50 Ω which is a convenient
match for most modern transmitters. The antenna impedance
however contains a large capacitive reactance and this is tuned out by
including a series loading coil at the base of the antenna (Figure 45).
This type of antenna needs to be operated against ground or a ground
plane and is popular as a mobile antenna for the VHF and UHF
bands. This type of antenna gives a gain of about 4 dB over a simple
dipole.

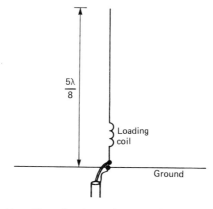

Figure 45   *A 5/8 wavelength vertical antenna with loading coil for*
matching and resonance

Loop antennas

As an alternative to the dipole a full wavelength loop may be used as an antenna. In the quad loop the wire is arranged as a square loop with sides of a quarter wavelength each and the antenna is fed at the centre of one side (Figure 46). For a delta loop the sides have a length of one-third of a wavelength and again the antenna is fed at the centre of one side (Figure 47). It is also possible to feed the antenna at one of its corners.

Side length for a quad loop antenna is given by:

$$\text{Length} = \frac{76}{f}\,\text{m or }\frac{251}{f}\,\text{ft}$$

Where f is frequency in MHz.

For a delta loop the total length around the loop is given by:

$$\text{Length} = \frac{302}{f}\,\text{m or }\frac{1005}{f}\,\text{ft}$$

For a quad antenna if the side being fed is horizontal then the polarization is horizontal while feeding a vertical side will give a vertically polarized signal. The feed impedance of a quad loop is approximately 120 Ω.

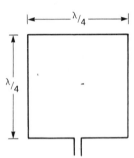

Figure 46   *The quad loop type antenna*

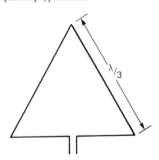

Figure 47   *The delta loop type antenna*

Beam antennas

By combining together a number of simple antennas, such as dipoles, it is possible to produce a very directional antenna which also exhibits considerable gain in signal over a single dipole in the direction of maximum radiation or pick-up. These beam antennas fall into two basic groups. In the first group the antennas are all driven from the transmitter and the signals to each antenna in the array are carefully phased relative to those in the other antennas so that the signal is reinforced in the main beam direction and cancelled in the other directions. The second type of beam antenna uses parasitic elements which are not fed directly by the transmitter but which re-radiate the signal that they themselves pick up from the driven antenna element.

Yagi arrays

In the Yagi type antenna a reflector element is mounted behind the dipole and one or more director elements may be mounted in front of the dipole (Figure 48). The reflector is a short-circuited dipole which is made slightly longer than half a wavelength. The effect of detuning the reflector is to alter the phase of the current induced in it by the signal radiated from the dipole. The current in the reflector causes it to radiate and if the phasing is correct this radiated signal will reinforce that of the dipole in one direction and cancel it in the other. The result is that radiation behind the reflector is reduced to give a directional beam in the direction of the dipole (Figure 49). If the parasitic element is shorter than the driven element it becomes a director and the beam is in the direction of the parasitic element. An antenna of this type is called a Yagi beam and typically will have a driven element, reflector and one or more directors.

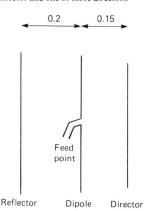

Figure 48   *Three element Yagi type beam antenna*

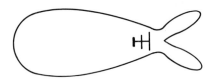

Figure 49   *Polar diagram for a simple Yagi beam antenna*

The optimum spacing of the reflector and directors is normally less than a quarter wave and typically the reflector is spaced at about 0·2 wavelength and the directors at 0·15 wavelength intervals. The antenna gain increases with the number of elements and the beam width becomes narrower. The length of the reflector is 1·05 times the dipole length and the first director is 0·95 times the dipole length. Extra directors are made progressively shorter by about 5 per cent for each director.

Parasitic beam antennas can also be built using quad or delta loop elements.

Transmission lines

In most transmitting stations the antenna is at some distance from the transmitter itself and some means of conveying the signal efficiently between transmitter and antenna is required. This link is provided by an antenna feeder which may be a cable or an open wire arrangement.

The transmission line has a characteristic impedance Z_o. If the line is terminated in a resistive load equal to Z_o it is correctly matched and the maximum amount of power is transferred along the line to the load. Under these conditions the load presented to the transmitter by the matched line is a pure resistance equal to Z_o.

Coaxial cable
For most applications the transmission line is a coaxial cable. This has a centre conductor and a concentric outer conductor (screen) which are separated by insulation (Figure 50). The characteristic impedance of the cable is determined by the geometry of the centre conductor and the outer screen and is given by:

$$Z_o = 138 \times \log \frac{D_o}{D_i} \, \Omega$$

Where D_i is the diameter of the inner conductor and D_o is the diameter of the outer conductor.

Typical coaxial cables have a characteristic impedance of either 50 or 75 Ω.

Losses in a coaxial cable depend upon the conductivity of the centre conductor and screen and the characteristics of the insulation between them. In low loss cables the insulator is made in the form of a helix so that most of the insulation is provided by air rather than solid plastic. In some cases the centre conductor may be silver plated or even solid silver to reduce losses. Attenuation is quoted in dB per

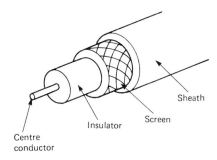

Figure 50 *Construction of a coaxial feeder cable*

10 m length of cable. Total power loss over a length of cable is given by:

$$\text{Total loss dB} = \frac{\text{length (m)} \times \text{attenuation (dB/10 m)}}{10} \, \text{dB}$$

The characteristics of some typical coaxial cables are as follows:

Type	Diameter mm	Z_0 Ω	pF/m	Attenuation 10 MHz	dB per 10 m 100 MHz
RGB	10·2	50	96	0·3	0·9
RG11	10·2	75	66	0·3	0·9
RG58C	5·0	50	100		2·0
RG59B	6·15	75	68		1·3
RG174A	2·8	50	100	1·1	2·8
RG178B	1·8	50	96	1·8	4·4
RG179B	2·5	75	64	1·9	3·2
UR43	5·0	50	100	0·7	1·3
UR67	10·3	50	100		0·7
UR70	5·8	75	67		1·5
UR76	5·0	50	100		1·6
UR95	2·3	50	100	0·9	2·7

Twin wire feeders

An alternative to coaxial cable is the twin wire feeder where two parallel wires are embedded in a flat ribbon cable (Figure 50). Standard cables are made with either 75 or 300 Ω impedance and their characteristics are:

Z_0 Ω	Width mm	pF/m	Attenuation 10 MHz	dB/10 m 1000 MHz
75	4·0	60	0·12	2·0
300	9·7	13	0·12	1·7

An air spaced twin feeder can be made by having two parallel wires held apart by insulating spacers at intervals along the line (Figure 51). Characteristic impedance of an air spaced parallel twin line is given by:

$$Z_o = 276 \times \log \frac{2S}{d}$$

Where S is the spacing between the wires and d is the conductor diameter.

Tuned feeders

An alternative to the conventional twin feeder is the use of a widely spaced pair of feeder wires which are tuned as part of the antenna system itself. In this case there is normally a standing wave on the feeders themselves but they do not radiate because the currents in the two wires are in opposite directions and the fields tend to cancel.

The feeders and the antenna system are tuned to resonance so that the impedance seen at the transmitter end is non-reactive and the antenna matching and tuning unit is then used to transform this impedance to match the output impedance of the power output stage of the transmitter.

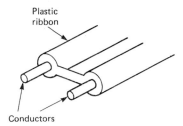

Figure 51   *Construction of a flat twin feeder ribbon cable*

Waveguides

At microwave frequencies the losses in coaxial cables become quite high so an alternative method of feeding the signals between the transmitter and the antenna is used. This makes use of a circular or rectangular section metal tube known as a *waveguide* (Figure 52). The electromagnetic wave is injected into the guide by a small probe or loop which effectively acts as an antenna and the wave is propagated along the guide by reflections from the walls. The metal tube merely serves to contain the wave as it is propagated from one end to the other. At the antenna end the waveguide is usually flared out to form a short horn which radiates or picks up the microwave signal.

Rectangular waveguides usually have a height (Y) which is equal to roughly half the width (X). The critical dimension for a wavelength is X for a rectangular type or radius (R) for a circular type. The range of wavelengths handled with the waveguide operating in its dominant mode is:

1·1–1·6 X for rectangular guide
2·8–3·2 R for circular guide

An X band waveguide is typically about 2·5 cm (1 in) wide and 1·25 cm (0·5 in) high. This gives wavelength range from 2·75 to 4 cm which corresponds to a frequency range from 7·5 to 11 GHz.

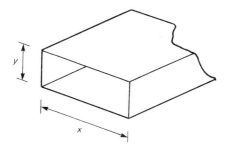

Rectangular waveguide

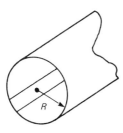

Circular waveguide

Figure 52   *Construction of rectangular and circular type waveguides for use at microwave frequencies*

Velocity factor

Radio waves travelling along a feeder cable have a velocity which is less than that of a wave in free space. The ratio between the velocity in a cable and that in free space is called the velocity factor and needs to be taken into account when cables are used to link several antennas operating as an array since the length of the link cables will determine the phasing of the feeds to the individual radiator elements.

Voltage standing wave ratio

When a transmission line is mismatched at one end some of the transmitted signal is reflected back along the line. This reflected signal varies in phase with the forward signal as it travels back along the line and the effect is that it will either add to or subtract from the forward signal thus producing a variation in the effective signal according to the position along the line. This produces what is known as a standing wave along the transmission line.

A convenient method of measuring the degree of mismatch between the line impedance and the load at the end of the line is that of measuring the relation between the forward signal and the reflected signal on the line. This measurement is known as the voltage standing wave ratio (VSWR) which is often referred to simply as the SWR. In an ideally matched line the VSWR is 1:1.

Two types of SWR meter are commonly used. In one type, known as a *reflectometer*, small samples of the forward and reflected wave are picked up from the line and fed to a bridge circuit which then drives a display meter. In the alternative type a transformer inserted into the line couples part of the signal to two power meter circuits which measure the forward and reflected power levels. In this type optimum matching occurs when the reflected power is at a minimum

BALUN

A symmetrical antenna such as a dipole will produce signals at its two terminals which are balanced relative to ground potential whereas a vertical antenna such as a ground plane provides a signal where one side of the signal source is at ground potential. Most transmitters and receivers have an unbalanced output or input in which one side of the signal is tied to ground potential. For optimum performance the dipole should be fed from a balanced signal source and this can be achieved by including a BALUN (balanced to unbalanced transformer) in the transmission line system. On the balanced side the centre tap point is grounded and the two feeds to the antenna operate in antiphase to give a balanced feed to the dipole or other balanced input antenna. The unbalanced input is fed between one end of the winding and the centre tap (Figure 53(a)).

If the windings are arranged to have equal turns the transformer provides an impedance transformation and the impedance at the balanced side will be four times that at the unbalanced side. If a 1:1 ratio is required then an extra winding is added (Figure 53(b)).

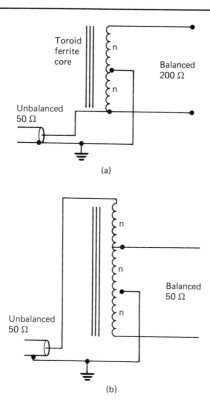

Figure 53   *Basic arrangement of a BALUN transformer:*
(a) *Simple type with 4:1 impedance ratio*
(b) *Modified type for 1:1 impedance ratio*

11
Transmitters

The internal arrangement of any transmitter can be broadly divided into two basic blocks (Figure 54). The first part is the *master oscillator* (MO) which generates radio frequency signals at the desired frequency. This block produces a relatively low power signal output so a *power amplifier* (PA) is used to raise the power level to provide the desired output power.

In a simple transmitter the MO section may be represented by a single stage oscillator with its frequency controlled by a quartz crystal. Although a crystal oscillator provides a stable output frequency it is not very flexible since the crystal must be changed to move to a new frequency. For more flexible operation nearly all amateur transmitters use a variable frequency oscillator (VFO) to generate the operating frequency signals. The VFO is usually tunable over a band of frequencies which might cover a complete amateur band such as 7·0–7·1 MHz. Many transmitters operate the VFO at relatively low frequency and then use frequency doubler circuits to raise the frequency to the desired value (Figure 55).

An alternative approach for producing the final frequency is to take the output signal from the VFO and mix it with a higher stable frequency from a quartz crystal oscillator (Figure 56). Thus if the VFO operates from 7·0–7·1 MHz and is mixed with a 43 MHz signal the result will be the sum frequency of 50·0–50·1 MHz which may then be used to drive a PA to give output on the six metre band.

Modern transceivers generally use some form of digital synthesizer circuit as the VFO followed by a mixer to shift the frequency to the desired band (Figure 57). In the synthesizer the VFO signal is fed to a digital counter circuit which eventually produces an output of perhaps 1 kHz. This counter output is compared in frequency with an accurate 1 kHz signal derived from a crystal oscillator. The output from the frequency comparator is used to electronically alter the tuning of the VFO so that the counter output is exactly 1 kHz. By varying the division ratio of the digital counter the frequency of the VFO can be altered.

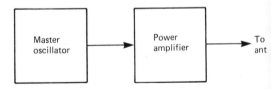

Figure 54   *Basic functional parts of a simple transmitter*

Figure 55   *Frequency generation using a VFO and frequency doubler system*

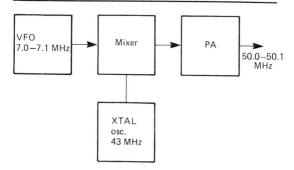

Figure 56   *Generation of high output frequencies using a VFO and a mixer system*

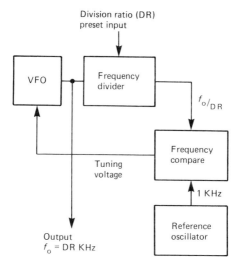

Figure 57   *Block diagram of a digital synthesizer*

Classes of operation

An amplifier may have different classes of operation according to the way in which it is biased. The class of operation is defined by the angle of the signal cycle over which the amplifier devices (valves or transistors) are conducting. A class A amplifier is one where conduction occurs throughout the entire signal cycle. Class B operation results when the amplifier devices conduct for one half cycle (180°). If the amplifier devices conduct for less than a half cycle the amplifier is a class C type. Amplifiers where the stages conduct for between 180° and 360° are called class AB types. In valve circuits, class AB1 circuits are those where no grid current is drawn while if grid current flows the amplifier is labelled as a class AB2 type.

Class A amplifiers have a maximum efficiency of 50 per cent so that half the input power is dissipated in the amplifier stage as heat. Class B and C amplifiers have best efficiencies of 65 per cent and 80 per cent which gives less heat dissipation for the same output power.

Frequency multipliers

A class C RF amplifier runs in a highly non-linear mode and produces a large amount of harmonic frequency output. By tuning the output circuits to twice the input frequency a frequency doubler can be produced. Tripler and quadrupler circuits can be produced in a similar way. For VHF and UHF operation the doubler or tripler action may be produced by simply rectifying the input RF signal and then selecting out the desired harmonic in the output tuned circuit.

On-off keying

For Morse telegraphy the normal technique is to simply key one of the driver stages of the power amplifier on and off by altering its bias conditions. In a few cases the key switch may actually be used to break the emitter or cathode circuit of the amplifier.

If switching of the amplifier is very rapid a problem that can occur is that of *key clicks* which are audible over a range of frequencies each side of the carrier frequency. To avoid this problem a key click filter is usually included in the key circuit. This is simply a low pass filter which rounds off the sharp edges of the switching signal (Figure 58).

A further problem is *chirp* which can occur when the VFO itself is keyed or where the supply voltage to the VFO varies when the output power stages are turned on. Chirp is caused by the frequency of the VFO being altered when the rest of the transmitter is keyed.

Amplitude modulation (A3E)

System of modulation in which the RF signal amplitude is varied in sympathy with the modulating waveform. The signal itself consists of a constant amplitude carrier component plus two sideband signals, one on each side of the carrier. The sidebands correspond to the sum and difference components of the carrier and the modulating frequency. Thus a 1 kHz tone modulating a 1 MHz carrier produces sideband frequencies of 999 and 1001 kHz.

Signal bandwidth for A3E is twice the highest modulating frequency. For typical voice signals of 300 Hz to 3 kHz the bandwidth required is 6 kHz.

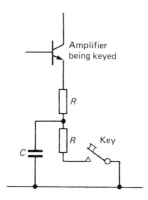

Figure 58 *Example of the inclusion of a low pass filter to eliminate key click problems*

Single sideband mode

Single sideband (SSB) transmissions refer to an amplitude modulated signal where the carrier component and one sideband have been suppressed before the signal is transmitted. The remaining sideband component still contains the information to be conveyed and at the receiving end an artificial carrier is inserted to enable the modulation component to be extracted.

Amateur stations transmit the lower sideband (LSB) on the 1·8, 3·5 and 7 MHz bands and the upper sideband (USB) on other bands up to 28 MHz. On VHF and UHF either sideband may be used but it seems that most stations use the USB mode.

Bandwidth is equal to the highest modulation frequency and for amateur telephony this is approximately 3 kHz.

Frequency modulation (F3E)

In frequency modulation the radiated frequency is varied in sympathy with the amplitude variations of the modulation signal. The frequency shift is called the *deviation* and is proportional to the amplitude of the modulating signal. The RF output power remains constant during the modulation cycle.

Bandwidth = $2 \times (M + D)$

Where D is the peak deviation and M is the highest modulating frequency.

For broadcasting wide band FM is used with a peak deviation of 75 kHz and audio signals up to 35 kHz giving a bandwidth of 220 kHz. Amateur and CB stations use narrow band FM with a peak deviation of 5 kHz and voice signals up to 3 kHz giving a bandwidth of about 16 kHz. Amateur FM channels at VHF are spaced at 25 kHz intervals to reduce adjacent channel interference.

$$\text{Modulation index} = \frac{D}{f_m}$$

Where D is the peak deviation and f_m is the modulating frequency.

The modulation index varies with modulation frequency and for a 250–2500 Hz voice signal and a 5 kHz deviation the MI ranges from 20 to 2.

$$\text{Deviation ratio} = \frac{D}{M}$$

Where D is peak deviation and M is the highest modulation frequency. For a typical VHF FM transmitter with 5 kHz deviation and audio up to 3 kHz the deviation ratio is 1·67.

Linear amplifiers

The frequency generation circuits of a transmitter are basically low power stages. When an SSB signal has been generated any following power amplifiers needed to produce the desired power output must operate in a linear fashion to avoid distortion of the signal and the generation of unwanted harmonics and other distortion products.

Most amateur radio transceivers generate about 100 W maximum PEP output so a high power linear amplifier is often added to increase the power output to the antenna to the permitted limit of 400 W PEP. Linear amplifiers are not essential for a CW or FM signal although they will generally produce much less trouble with harmonics and interference than a non-linear power stage.

For a linear amplifier using a single valve or transistor class A operation must be used. If a push pull circuit using a pair of valves or transistors is used the class AB or class B modes may be used to give higher efficiency.

Overmodulation

If the modulation signal is increased to the level where it causes the RF output to switch off or saturate on peaks of modulation the transmission is said to be overmodulated. The effect is the same as clipping off the peaks of the modulating signal and this has the effect of introducing harmonics of the modulating signal. The result is that the sidebands of the radiated signal extend far beyond the range needed for the normal modulation frequencies. This has the effect of producing *splatter* which may extend over a large part of the band and cause interference to other users. Similar problems may also be produced on an FM signal which has been overmodulated.

Speech processing

Normal speech consists of peaks of signal but the average signal level is quite low so that for most of the time the modulation depth is quite low. By increasing the audio gain or talking louder the output can be increased but overmodulation will occur on voice peaks. To overcome this some amateurs use speech processor circuits. The main part of a speech processor is that automatic gain control is applied to the audio amplifier so that the peaks of the signal are compressed and the average signal level is increased without causing overmodulation. The effect of this is to produce an audio signal with more 'punch' which will tend to stand out particularly under difficult propagation conditions. Many speech processors also modify the audio frequency range to produce the most effective voice signal. Generally speech processing should only be used under difficult contact conditions and is not normally required for ordinary contacts.

Carrier power

Carrier power can be measured by measuring the RF output voltage across the transmitter load. This assumes either a dummy load or a correctly matched antenna as a load.

$$\text{Carrier power} = \frac{V_O{}^2}{L_L}\text{Watts}$$

Where V_O is RMS output voltage and R_L is load resistance in Ω.

Peak envelope power

The peak envelope power (PEP) is the power output at the peak of a modulated wave. This method of measuring power output is used for SSB transmissions where there is no steady carrier power output.

$$\text{PEP} = 0.5 \times \frac{V_P{}^2}{R_L}\text{Watts}$$

Where V_P is the peak output voltage at peak of the modulation cycle and R_L is the load resistance.

Electromagnetic compatibility

The electromagnetic compatibility (EMC) for a transmitter is largely concerned with its capability of interfering with other users of the radio spectrum. The major potential causes of interference are the radiation of harmonic signals and radiation due to parasitic oscillations within the power stages of the transmitter.

Harmonic radiation can be reduced to acceptable levels by operating the amplifier stages in linear modes such as class A or class B or by inserting low pass filters between the final amplifier and the antenna to suppress harmonics of the wanted output frequency.

Parasitic oscillation in the power stages can be overcome by careful design of the amplifier layout and the inclusion of small RF chokes into the input and output circuits to break up potential feedback paths for high frequency signals.

A major interference problem is caused by breakthrough. In this case the transmitter is radiating only the desired output but the strong local fields can cause problems in poorly designed consumer equipment such as radios, hi-fi units and video recorders. Here the strong transmitter signal is picked up on unscreened wiring and rectified by semiconductor devices such as transistors or diodes. This can produce either harmonic signals or demodulated audio within the consumer equipment which interferes with its operation.

In many cases breakthrough is caused by pickup of RF on aerial feeder cables or mains leads and this can often be dealt with by inserting suitable filters in these leads. A braid-breaker filter in the aerial lead of a TV set often cures breakthrough problems from a HF transmitter. In the case of hi-fi equipment the problem can be more difficult and may involve actual modifications to the equipment. This should not be attempted by the amateur and is the responsibility of the manufacturer or supplier of the equipment.

The RSGB has available a number of filters which are useful in dealing with EMC problems. Details of these filters are as follows:

BB1   Braid-breaker type suitable for use with UHF TV receivers and VHF FM receivers. Similar to British Telecom filter FS74a.

HPF2   High pass filter designed for use with FM radio receivers. May also be used in conjunction with filter BB1 in severe cases.

HPF1   Combined braid-breaker and high pass filter for use with UHF TV receivers. Similar to British Telecom filter FS72a.

TNF2/2   This is a notch filter designed to reject 144 MHz signals and suitable for use with UHF TV and VHF FM receivers. Similar to British Telecom filter FS64/1a.

TNF1/70   This is a notch filter designed to reject 432 MHz signals and suitable for use with UHF TV receivers. Similar to British Telecom filter type FS73a.

12
Receivers

Tuned radio frequency receiver

Figure 59 shows the block diagram for a simple tuned radio
frequency (TRF) or *straight* receiver. Signals from the antenna are
amplified by one or more radio frequency amplifier stages then
demodulated to give an audio signal. The audio signal is then
amplified to drive a loudspeaker.

The RF amplifier stages are tuned by variable capacitors which are
ganged together to ensure that all stages remain tuned to the desired
signal frequency. For amplitude modulated signals the detector is
basically a half wave rectifier followed by a low pass filter to remove
the high frequency carrier signals.

The main disadvantages of this type of receiver are the difficulties
in obtaining good selectivity and sensitivity. Positive feedback
(regeneration) may be applied to the demodulator stage to increase
gain and selectivity in a TRF receiver.

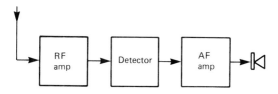

Figure 59   *Block diagram of a tuned radio frequency (TRF) type
receiver*

Superheterodyne receivers

The most widely used type of receiver today is the superheterodyne or
superhet shown in block form in Figure 60. In a superhet the
incoming signal (f_c) is mixed with a local oscillator signal (f_o) to

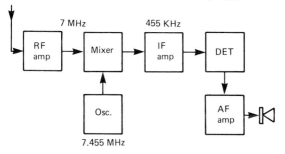

Figure 60   *Block diagram of a superheterodyne receiver*

produce a difference frequency component $(f_o - f_c)$ which is called the intermediate frequency (IF) (Figure 61). The local oscillator is generally set at a higher frequency than the signal being received. Most of the amplification and selectivity is provided in the IF amplifier which operates at a fixed frequency. The IF amplifier output is then demodulated to produce audio or video output. The local oscillator tuning is tracked with the desired input signal so that the difference between the two remains constant and equal to the IF. The actual frequency used for the IF amplifier varies according to the application but the following values are commonly used.

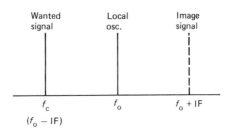

Figure 61   *Illustration of the relationship between the signal, image and local oscillator frequencies*

Intermediate frequency	Application
455 kHz	MF and HF broadcast receiver
1·6 MHz	First IF in double superhet
8·8 MHz	Amateur radio transceivers
10·7 MHz	VHF FM receivers
33–39 MHz	UHF TV receivers
35–70 MHz	Amateur radio transceivers
70 MHz	Satellite TV second IF
800 MHz	Satellite TV first IF

Image interference

In a superhet receiver with the oscillator above the signal frequency an input signal with a frequency of $f_o + F_{if}$ will also produce a mixer output at the intermediate frequency and this will interfere with the wanted signal. This form of interference is called *second channel* or *image* interference. In a typical broadcast superhet with an IF of 455 kHz this form of interference is a major problem at signal frequencies above 10 MHz unless several highly selective RF stages are used ahead of the mixer.

Double conversion superhet

The simplest solution to image interference is to use a higher value of intermediate frequency. Unfortunately with a higher IF it is more difficult to achieve good selectivity with conventional tuned circuits.

To overcome these problems a double conversion system may be used (Figure 62). The first mixer produces an IF of, say, 1·6 MHz which eliminates problems with image interference. The first IF signal is then fed to a second mixer which produces a 455 kHz IF. The lower 455 kHz IF can be used to provide most of the required amplification and selectivity.

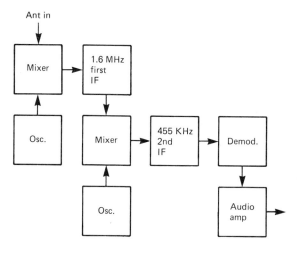

Figure 62   *Double conversion superheterodyne receiver*

Wadley loop system

One problem with superhet receivers, particularly at higher frequencies when using a narrow bandwidth IF, is that the local oscillator frequency will drift with temperature causing loss of signal and the need for retuning. The Wadley loop is a double conversion scheme which is designed to reduce the effects of drift in the local oscillator (Figure 63).

The signal is first up converted to an IF which is higher than the highest input frequency. This signal is then down converted to the second IF using a crystal controlled oscillator. Any drift in the first local oscillator will produce a drift in the first IF frequency but the down conversion produces a drift in the second IF which is in the opposite direction so that the two effects tend to cancel out.

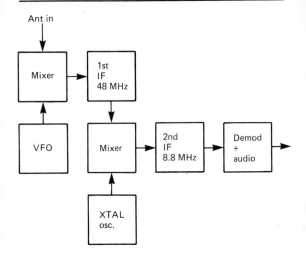

Figure 63 *Superheterodyne receiver using the Wadley loop scheme to reduce the effects of frequency drift in the local oscillator*

Most modern amateur radio transceivers use this technique with the first IF in the region 35–65 MHz and the second IF in the region of 8–9 MHz. Some receivers use a triple conversion scheme in which the 8 MHz second IF is converted again to a 455 kHz IF for the final amplification and demodulation stages.

Digital synthesizers

In older receivers the tunable local oscillator uses a standard stable oscillator circuit. With the advent of integrated circuits it is more common to find receivers fitted with digital frequency synthesizers to generate the local oscillator frequency. The synthesizer output is from a voltage controlled oscillator (VCO). The output of the VCO is also fed to a digital frequency divider chain which has a variable division ratio. The output from the frequency divider is compared with a crystal controlled reference oscillator and the phase or frequency difference signal is fed back to control the frequency of the VCO. The oscillator frequency will settle down at a frequency of D times the reference frequency where D is the division ratio of the frequency divider. By varying the division ratio the desired output frequency from the VCO can be set up. A frequency synthesizer of this type provides a very stable oscillator and the frequency can readily be displayed on a digital display.

CW and SSB reception

For the reception of CW and SSB signals a local carrier signal needs to be re-inserted at the demodulator stage to render the signals intelligible. For CW the injected signal is set about 800 Hz to 1 kHz away from the frequency of the signal being received so that the output becomes pulses of audio tone. For SSB reception the local carrier must be injected at the frequency where the suppressed carrier should be so that the signal can be demodulated.

For CW and SSB reception with a TRF receiver the regeneration is advanced to the point where oscillation occurs and this provides a beat tone for CW and a re-inserted carrier for SSB reception.

Direct conversion receivers

The direct conversion receiver is basically a superheterodyne which has an intermediate frequency of zero. The incoming signal is mixed with a local oscillator of the same frequency as the received signal. The output from the mixer is fed directly to the audio amplifier stages of the receiver. In this type of receiver the selectivity is determined by the frequency response of the audio amplifier circuits.

For SSB reception the local oscillator need only be within a few cycles of the signal frequency to give acceptable output. This type of receiver is usually called a *homodyne* (Figure 65). For CW reception the local oscillator is set about 800 Hz away from the incoming CW carrier to provide a suitable audio frequency tone.

For conventional AM reception the local oscillator must be phase locked to the incoming carrier to avoid 'growling' or beat frequency tones. This may be achieved by using a phase locked loop integrated circuit such as the NE561B as the local oscillator. This type of receiver with a synchronized local oscillator is called a *synchrodyne*.

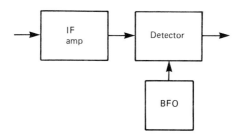

Figure 64   *Use of a beat frequency oscillator (BFO) for receiving CW or SSB signals*

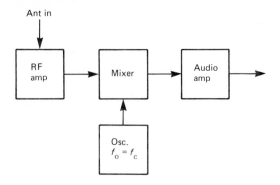

Figure 65   *Block diagram of a Homodyne receiver*

Signal strength unit

Nominally, a signal strength unit (S unit) is equivalent to a 6 dB
increase in signal level at the receiver input. The scale runs from S_0 to
S_9 with the S_9 level usually set for an input signal of 50 μV at the
antenna input terminals. Actual receiver S meters normally extend
beyond the S_9 level. Readings above S_9 are quoted as $S_9 + n$ dB and
scales are usually marked up to $S_9 + 60$ dB.

Sensitivity

Sensitivity is normally quoted as the input in microvolts required to
produce a signal + noise to noise ratio of 10 dB. A good HF
communications receiver will generally have a sensitivity figure of
about 0·15 μV for SSB operation with a 3 kHz bandwidth. For FM
operation with its wider bandwidth a sensitivity figure of about
0·5 μV might be expected.

Selectivity

The selectivity of a receiver is its ability to reject signals on adjacent
frequencies to the desired signal frequency. The pass band is the
bandwidth over which the signal voltage falls in amplitude by less
than 3 dB. The skirt selectivity is also important since it defines the
rate at which the unwanted signals are attenuated outside the pass
band. Typically skirt selectivity is the bandwidth outside which
signals are rejected by at least 60 dB. A good response is one where
the skirt bandwidth is only a little wider than the passband.

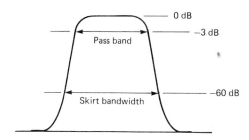

Figure 66   *Frequency response of a typical IF amplifier showing the pass band and skirt selectivity*

13
Components

Colour codes

On many resistors and capacitors the value is indicated by a colour code rather than by figures. On most modern resistors the colour coding consists of a series of coloured rings but on some older resistors the body colour represents the first digit of the value. The value is given by the first two coloured rings with the third ring indicating the multiplier factor as follows:

Colour	Number	Multiplier
Black	0	× 1
Brown	1	× 10
Red	2	× 100
Orange	3	× 1000
Yellow	4	× 10 000
Green	5	× 100 000
Blue	6	× 1 000 000
Purple	7	× 10 000 000
Grey	8	× 100 000 000
White	9	× 1 000 000 000
Silver	—	× 0·01
Gold	—	× 0·1

A fourth band may be used to indicate tolerance as follows:

Brown	± 1%	Silver	± 10%
Red	± 2%	None	± 20%
Gold	± 5%		

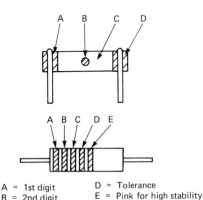

A = 1st digit   D = Tolerance
B = 2nd digit   E = Pink for high stability
C = Multiplier

Figure 67 *Resistor colour code markings*

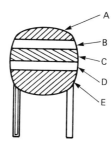

A First digit
B Second digit
C Multiplier (based on PF units)
D Tolerance
E Working voltage

Figure 68 *Capacitor colour code markings*

Preferred values

For resistors and capacitors a series of preferred values is normally
used. For the wider tolerance components a subset of the full series is
generally used. The two common series of values in use are the E12
and E24 series of values.

E6 series
1·0, 1·5, 2·2, 3·3, 4·7 and 6·8.

E12 series
1·0, 1·2, 1·5, 1·8, 2·2, 2·7, 3·3, 3·9, 4·7, 5·6, 6·8 and 8·2.

E24 series
1·0, 1·1, 1·2, 1·3, 1·5, 1·6, 1·8, 2·0, 2·2, 2·4, 2·7, 3·0, 3·3, 3·6, 3·9, 4·3, 4·7,
5·1, 5·6, 6·2, 6·8, 7·5, 8·2 and 9·1.

Resistor codes

On circuit diagrams and on some components the resistor value is
given as a numerical code rather than as a full value. The system uses
a letter combined with the preferred value. This letter indicates the
multiplier as follows:

R = Ω
K = kΩ
M = MΩ

Thus 4R7 represents a value of $4.7\,\Omega$ and:

$47R = 47\,\Omega$
$470R = 470\,\Omega$
$4K7 = 4700\,\Omega$
$47K = 47\,k\Omega$
$4M7 = 4.7\,M\Omega$

A letter following the value code indicates the resistor tolerance as follows:

$F = 1\%$
$G = 2\%$
$J = 5\%$
$K = 10\%$
$M = 20\%$

Capacitor value codes

Standard preferred values as for resistors.

Multiplier codes

Picofarad	pF
Nanofarad (1000 pF)	nF
Microfarad (1000 nF)	μF

Examples

Marking	Value
p47	0·47 pF
4p7	4·7 pF
47p	47 pF
4n7	4700 pF
47n	0·047 μF
470n	0·47 μF
4μ7	4·7 μF

Values less than 1000 pF marked in pF and above $1\,\mu$F in μF.

Some capacitors are marked with a two figure value in pF followed by a third figure which is a power of 10 multiplier.

$$473 = 47 \times 10^3 = 47\,000\,\text{pF or } 0.047\,\mu\text{F}$$

Resistance calculations

Resistors in series:

$$R = R_1 + R_2$$

Resistors in parallel:

$$R = \frac{R_1 \times R_2}{R_1 + R_2}$$

Capacitance calculations

Capacitors in series:

$$C = \frac{C_1 \times C_2}{C_1 + C_2}$$

Capacitors in parallel:

$$C = C_1 + C_2$$

Capacitive reactance:

$$X_C = \frac{1}{2\pi f C}\ \Omega$$

Capacitance of parallel plate capacitor:

$$C = \frac{0\cdot885\ KA}{d.}\text{pF}$$

Where A is the plate area in cm^2, d is the spacing in cm and K is the dielectric constant of insulator (for air insulation $K = 1$).

Inductance calculations

Inductors in series:

$$L = L_1 + L_2$$

Inductors in parallel:

$$L = \frac{L_1 \times L_2}{L_1 + L_2}$$

Inductive reactance:

$$X_L = 2\pi f L\ \Omega$$

Inductance of air cored coils:

$$L = \frac{a^2 n^2}{9a + 10b}$$

Where n is the number of turns, a is the radius of coil in in, b is the length of coil in in, and L is the inductance of coil in μH.

Number of turns required for inductance $L\mu$H:

$$n = \sqrt{\frac{9a + 10b}{La^2}}$$

Component symbols

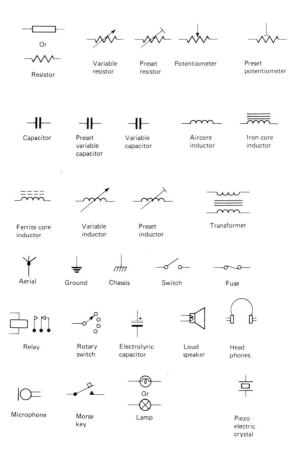

Figure 69 *Common component symbols for use in circuit diagrams*

Semiconductor symbols

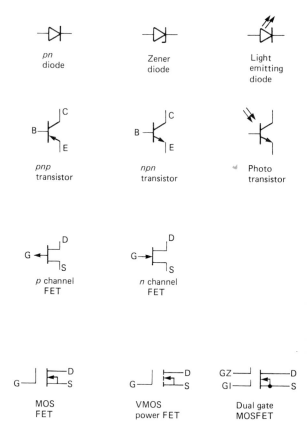

Figure 70   *Semiconductor device symbols*

Logic device symbols

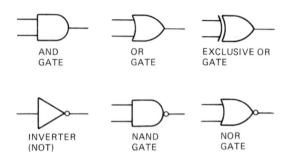

| AND GATE | OR GATE | EXCLUSIVE OR GATE |
| INVERTER (NOT) | NAND GATE | NOR GATE |

Figure 71 *Symbols used to represent logic gates*

Copper wire table

SWG number	Diameter (in)	Turns per in	Turns per cm	Ohms per 10 ft
16	0·064	15·0	5·9	0·025
18	0·048	19·8	7·8	0·044
20	0·036	26·1	10·2	0·079
22	0·028	33·3	13·1	0·13
24	0·022	42·1	16·6	0·21
26	0·018	50·6	19·9	0·32
28	0·0148	61·4	24·2	0·47
30	0·0124	73·3	28·9	0·66
32	0·0108	83·0	32·7	0·88
34	0·0092	98·0	38·6	1·21
36	0·0076	116·0	45·7	1·77
38	0·006	143·0	56·3	2·83
40	0·0048	180·0	70·9	4·40

Decibel power ratios

Power ratio (dB) $= 10 \times \log_{10} \dfrac{P_1}{P_2}$

Where P_1 and P_2 are the powers being compared and P_2 is the reference power.

Figures given as dB W are related to a reference power of 1 W.

dB value	Power ratio	
	+ dB	− dB
0	1·0	1·0
1	1·3	0·8
2	1·6	0·6
3	2·0	0·5
4	2·5	0·4
5	3·2	0·3
6	4·0	0·25
7	5·0	0·2
8	6·3	0·16
9	8·0	0·125
10	10	0·1
20	100	0·01
30	1000	0·001
40	10^4	10^{-4}
50	10^5	10^{-5}
60	10^6	10^{-6}
70	10^7	10^{-7}
80	10^8	10^{-8}
90	10^9	10^{-9}
100	10^{10}	10^{-10}

For intermediate values take the ratio for the nearest 10 dB and multiply by the ratio for the units dB figure. Thus + 26 dB relative to 1 W gives:

$$100 \quad \times 4·0 \quad \times 1 \quad = 400\,W$$
$$(20\,dB) \quad (6\,dB) \quad (P_2) \quad (P_2 + 26\,dB)$$

14
Useful magazines and books

Magazines

Radio Communication (monthly)
RSGB, Cranborne Road, Potters Bar, Hertfordshire.

Ham Radio Today (monthly)
ASP Ltd, 1 Golden Square, London W1R 3AB.

Amateur Radio (monthly)
Sovereign House, Brentwood, Essex CM14 4SE

Radio & Electronics World (monthly)
Sovereign House, Brentwood, Essex CM14 4SE

Practical Wireless (monthly)
Enefco House, The Quay, Poole, Dorset.

Short Wave Magazine (monthly)
Enefco House, The Quay, Poole, Dorset.

CQ-TV (monthly)
BATC Publications, 14 Lilac Avenue, Leicester LE5 1FN.

QST (monthly)
ARRL, 225 Main Street, Newington, Connecticut, USA.

73 Magazine (monthly)
73 Magazine, Pine Street, Peterborough, New Hampshire, USA.

Ham Radio (monthly)
Communications Technology Inc., Greenville, New Hampshire, USA.

Citizen's Band (monthly)
ASP Ltd, 1 Golden Square, London W1R 3AB.

Books
Amateur radio
Radio Communication Handbook
ARRL, Newington, Connecticut, USA.

Radio Communication Handbook
RSGB, Potters Bar, Hertfordshire.

Amateur Radio Operating Manual
RSGB, Potters Bar, Hertfordshire.

Radio Amateur Examination Manual
RSGB, Potters Bar, Hertfordshire.

Amateur Radio Software
RSGB, Potters Bar, Hertfordshire.

AX25 Amateur Packet Radio Protocol
ARRL, Newington, Connecticut, USA.

Radio Wave Propagation
F. C. Judd, Heinemann-Newnes, London.

Picture transmission
Guide to Facsimile Stations
J. Klingenfuss, Klingenfuss Publications.

Amateur Television Handbook
BATC

Slow Scan Companion
BATC

Utility stations
Guide to Utility Stations
J. Klingenfuss, Klingenfuss Publications.

Radioteletype Code Manual
J. Klingenfuss, Klingenfuss Publications.

Air & Meteo Code Manual
J. Klingenfuss, Klingenfuss Publications.

Radioteletype Press Broadcasts
M. Schaay, Schaay Publishers, Doorn, Holland.

US Military Radio Communications
M. Schaay, Schaay Publishers, Doorn, Holland.

Radio Hackers Code Book
G. Soussoon, Duckworth Books, London.

UK Listener's Confidential Frequency List
B. Laver, Waters & Stanton, Hockley, Essex.

HF Oceanic Airband Communications
B. Laver, Waters & Stanton, Hockley, Essex.

Guide to VHF/UHF Frequencies 26–2250 MHz
Waters & Stanton, Hockley, Essex.

VHF/UHF Airband Frequency Guide
Waters & Stanton, Hockley, Essex.

Scanners–VHF/UHF Listener Guide
P. Rouse, Argus Books, London.

Satellites
Communications Satellites
L. van Horn, Grove Enterprises, Brasstown NC, USA.

Satellite Experimenter's Handbook
M. Davidoff, ARRL, Newington, Connecticut, USA.

Fuji FO12 Technical Handbook
AMSAT–UK.

Oscar 10 Technical Handbook
AMSAT–UK.

Guide to OSCAR operation
AMSAT–UK.

Books from Klingenfuss and Schaay are available from Interbooks, Stanley, Perth, Scotland PH1 4QQ.

ARRL books are available from the RSGB.

15

Useful addresses

Radio Society of Great Britain (RSGB), Lambda House, Cranborne Road, Potters Bar, Hertfordshire.

Amateur Radio Relay League (ARRL), Main Street, Newington, Connecticut, USA.

Waters & Stanton Ltd, 18–20 Main Road, Hockley, Essex.

AMSAT–UK, Ron Broadbent, 94 Herongate Road, Wanstead Park, London E12 5EQ.

British Amateur Radio Teleprinter Group (BARTG), Mr J. Beedie, 'Ffynnonlas', Salem, Llandeilo, Dyfed.

British Amateur Television Club (BATC), Mr D. Lawton, 'Grenehurst', Pinewood Road, High Wycombe, Buckinghamshire.

The 934 MHz Club UK, Mrs G. Anthony, PO Box 424, Althorne, Chelmsford, Essex.

16

QSL cards

Most amateur radio stations exchange QSL (acknowledgement of receipt) cards to confirm their contacts. These cards are normally postcard size and give details of the contact. Many are very attractively designed and some amateurs display their QSL cards on the wall of their radio room or 'shack'. QSL cards are often requested as verification of the contacts made when an amateur claims one of the many operating awards that are available.

Many broadcast stations and some utility stations will also send QSL cards to confirm a reception report sent in by a listener.

17
Contests and awards

During the year there are many operating contests in which radio amateurs can take part. Many are organized by national amateur radio societies and provide an opportunity for stations of that country to work with other amateurs around the world. The usual effect of any contest is to increase the level of activity thus making it possible for amateurs to contact the rarer stations.

In most contests the contact is very short and consists normally of exchange of a report and perhaps a serial number. In the CQ Worldwide contests the CQ zone numbers are exchanged. Points are scored for each contact made with additional points for stations in another continent or for working particular areas of the country sponsoring the contest. In some contests the number of countries or zones worked may provide bonus points and extra points may be available for working on several bands. Details of the contact and scoring procedures are usually available from the sponsoring club. Many stations make contacts in a contest but do not send in an official entry. Those that send in an entry usually have to send a copy of the log for the contest period together with any serial numbers or other confirmation details for each contact made. The RSGB publishes details and rules for many of the major contests in its magazine *Radio Communication*.

Apart from the major worldwide contests there are also more local contests, often carried out on the VHF or UHF bands, and aimed at increasing activity levels. Some of these contests operate over several periods during the year and the scores are cumulative with the winners being announced at the end of the year.

There are many awards which can be obtained in amateur radio. These usually require that the station claiming the award shall have worked a number of specified stations either in different countries, areas of one country or perhaps those who are members of a particular society. For many of the major awards QSL cards must be obtained as proof of contact and these are sent off with the claim for the award. For many awards, particularly those arranged by local radio clubs, a copy of the log entries, certified as correct by another radio amateur, is often sufficient.

A few of the many awards available are:

Worked all continents (WAC)
Organized by the IARU. Contacts must be made with each of the six continental areas of the world (Europe, Asia, Africa, North America, South America and Oceania). Special endorsements are available for making all contacts on one band or by a specific mode such as RTTY, fAX, SSTV or SSB.

DX Century Club Award (DXCC)
Organized by ARRL. Contacts required with 100 different countries as defined by the ARRL DXCC countries list. QSL cards are required for proof of contact. Additional awards to be added to the original DXCC award can be obtained by working 200 or 300 countries. A separate five band DXCC award can be obtained for working 100 countries on each of five bands since January 1969.

Worked all states (WAS)
This award requires contacts with stations in all fifty states of the
USA. Contacts may be on any band or any mode but special
endorsements are available for WAS using one mode (CW, SSB,
RTTY, etc.) or for contacts all on one band. A special five band WAS
award is available for working all fifty states on each of five bands.

Worked all zones (WAZ)
This award issued by *CQ Magazine* requires contacts with all forty
CQ zones. QSL cards are required for confirmation of contacts.

Worked ITU zones (WITUZ)
For contacts with land based stations in at least seventy different ITU
zones. Requires QSL cards and is issued by RSGB. There is also a five
band version of this award.

Worked British Commonwealth
Requires contacts with British Commonwealth stations in five
continents (Europe, Asia, Africa, America and Oceania). North and
South America count as one continent for this award.

Index

TANDIL, Argentina

LUAZ JW